THERMOELASTICITY

A BLAISDELL BOOK IN SOLID MECHANICS

CONSULTING EDITORS
William Prager, *University of California at San Diego*
Joseph Kestin, *Brown University*

THERMOELASTICITY

HEINZ PARKUS

INSTITUTE OF TECHNOLOGY
VIENNA, AUSTRIA

BLAISDELL PUBLISHING COMPANY

A DIVISION OF GINN AND COMPANY

Waltham, Massachusetts · Toronto · London

186341

Preface

THERMOELASTICITY—the generalization of elasticity to nonisothermal deformations—has made considerable progress during the last two decades. Its basic theory is now well established, and many applications to problems in engineering have been successfully made.

In writing this book it has been my aim to give, in a relatively small volume, an up-to-date presentation of those parts of thermoelasticity which, in my opinion, are of basic importance in the field. The theoretical background, together with the corresponding methods of solution, is developed first in each chapter and is followed by carefully selected examples intended to serve not only as illustrations of the theory but also as sources for useful results of engineering interest.

Following a brief introductory chapter, the linearized, uncoupled theory is presented. Frequent reference is made here to the theory of isothermal elasticity. A short review of the theory of heat conduction is included. The third and fourth chapters are concerned with special cases: plane thermoelastic stress and strain, and thermal bending and buckling of plates, respectively. The real function method and the complex function approach are introduced simultaneously in Chapter 3 in order to exhibit and delineate the respective merits of the two procedures. In Chapter 5 the theory of thermoelasticity is developed in its most general form. Several particular cases are considered. This chapter also provides a rigorous foundation for the linearized theory of the preceding chapters. Finally, as an application of the general theory, the propagation of one-dimensional plane waves in a medium conducting heat is studied. Each chapter is followed by a number of problems.

As a prerequisite for the study of the book, the reader is expected to have completed a course in the theory of elasticity, and to have some knowledge of what is usually termed advanced mathematics. The elements of complex function theory will be needed for an understanding of parts of Chapter 3.

It is my pleasant duty to record my sincere thanks to Dr. Herbert Bednarczyk, Dr. Josef L. Zeman, and Dr. Franz Ziegler, of my institute, for their interest and help in the preparation of the manuscript. My particular thanks are due to Professor William Prager for his invitation to write this book.

Vienna   HEINZ PARKUS

Contents

THERMOELASTICITY

CHAPTER 1

Introduction

THERMOELASTICITY describes the behavior of elastic bodies under the influence of nonuniform temperature fields. It represents, therefore, a generalization of the Theory of Elasticity. The constitutive equations, i.e., the equations characterizing the particular material, are temperature-dependent and include an additional relation connecting the heat flux in the body with the local temperature gradient. This relation, known in its simplest form as *Fourier's* law, determines the temperature distribution in the body.

Stress, strain, and temperature are interrelated in a very complicated manner. The exact solution of problems of general thermoelasticity presents, therefore, enormous difficulties, and the number of known solutions is very small. Chapter 5 is devoted to this general theory. Fortunately, however, drastic simplifications of the basic equations are possible in many cases of practical interest.

Suppose that temperature changes and deformations are small. The basic equations may then be linearized with respect to stress, strain, and tempera-ture in a manner similar to that of isothermal elasticity. Also, the heat produced within the body by the small deformations will itself be very small and, except for some special cases,† may be neglected. The basic equations then decouple: the equation of heat conduction separates from the remaining relations and the temperature field may be determined independently of stress and strain. Finally, temperature changes within the body will, in general, be slow, and the corresponding deformations will proceed slowly.‡

---

† See Chapter 6.
‡ As one exception, the case known as "thermal shock," which involves extremely rapid changes of the surface temperature, should be mentioned. However, such rapid changes do not occur frequently in practical problems and are difficult to produce in experiments.

Inertia effects are then negligible.† Thus, we arrive at what is known as "thermoelasticity of small deformations and small and slow temperature changes." Chapters 2 to 4 are restricted to this simplified theory.

Although interest in thermoelastic phenomena dates as far back as 1837, when Duhamel published his famous *Mémoire sur les phénomènes thermo-mécaniques*, it is only during the last two or three decades that active and systematic research has been conducted. The theory has now reached a certain completeness, but much still remains to be done in its application to engineering problems.

---

† This, of course, is not true if vibration or wave propagation problems are considered as in Chapter 6.

CHAPTER 2

The Linearized Theory

L IKE ANY OTHER THEORY in nonrelativistic mechanics of continua, thermoelasticity rests on three basic laws or axioms: the law of motion, the theorem of conservation of mass, and the theorem of conservation of energy. In Chapter 5, we shall have opportunity to dwell on these concepts and their implications in some detail and also from a very general point of view. At present, however, we are satisfied to confine our attention to the much less general, but practically very usable and important theory designated in Chapter 1 as "thermoelasticity of small deformations and of small and slow temperature changes."

2.1. Basic Equations

By small deformations we mean deformations that are small relative to the dimensions of the body. No distinction between the deformed and unde-formed body need then be made in formulating the equations of motion. Small temperature changes are changes small in comparison with the absolute initial reference temperature. Strain is then assumed to depend linearly on stress and temperature, and the equation of heat conduction will be the usual Fourier equation. Also, since heat conduction is a gradual process, the corresponding deformations will be slow. Inertia effects may therefore be neglected and the equations of motion reduce to the equations of equilibrium. This means that, following the slow change in temperature, the body moves slowly through a continuous sequence of positions of equilibrium without any significant acceleration. This is termed *quasistatic motion*.

In a rectangular cartesian coordinate frame (x, y, z) with stress tensor σ_{ij}, the equations of translational equilibrium are†

$$\sum_j \frac{\partial \sigma_{ji}}{\partial j} = 0 \qquad (i, j = x, y, z), \qquad (2.1)$$

while rotational equilibrium requires $\sigma_{ij} = \sigma_{ji}$.

The theorem of conservation of mass in the linearized theory reduces simply to

$$\rho = \rho_0, \qquad (2.2)$$

where ρ_0 is the initial and ρ the instantaneous mass density.

The behavior of an elastic material (i.e., the relation between stress σ_{ij} and strain ε_{ij}) is most conveniently characterized by its *elastic potential W* which may be defined by the relation‡

$$\sigma_{ij} = \frac{\partial W}{\partial \varepsilon_{ij}}. \qquad (2.3)$$

In contrast to isothermal elasticity, in thermoelasticity W not only depends on the strain components ε_{ij}, but also on the temperature T. The functional dependence is determined by the properties of the material. If W is a quadratic form [see Equation (2.9)], then, according to Equation (2.3), stress σ_{ij} will be related linearly to ε_{ij} and T. Thus we see that the generalized Hooke's law will be valid. Obviously, this is the only stress-strain law admissible in a linear theory.

Let $T = T_0 + \Theta$ be the temperature in a body initially at uniform temperature T_0. The temperature increase Θ will cause a line element ds to increase its length to $(1 + \alpha\Theta)\, ds$ provided it can expand freely. The symbol α represents the coefficient of (linear) thermal expansion. In the isotropic case to be considered here, α is a scalar. If the temperature increase is uniform, the body will simply increase its volume, but will remain stress-free. On the other hand, in a nonuniform temperature field stresses generally will be created. The components of strain may, therefore, be divided into two parts. The first, due to the temperature change, is given by

$$\varepsilon_{xx}^{(1)} = \varepsilon_{yy}^{(1)} = \varepsilon_{zz}^{(1)} = \alpha\Theta, \qquad \varepsilon_{xy}^{(1)} = \varepsilon_{yz}^{(1)} = \varepsilon_{zx}^{(1)} = 0.$$

---

† The derivation of these equations may be found, for instance, in [1] p. 40, and [2]. See also Section 5.3. Stresses from body forces are not included here. Due to the linearity of the equations they may be obtained independently in accordance with the principle of superposition.
‡ See Chapter 5.

The second part is produced by the stresses σ_{ij} and is equal to

$$\varepsilon_{xx}^{(2)} = \frac{1}{2G}\left(\sigma_{xx} - \frac{\nu}{1+\nu}s\right), \qquad \varepsilon_{xy}^{(2)} = \frac{\sigma_{xy}}{2G},$$

and so on, where G is the shear modulus, ν is Poisson's ratio, and s is the first invariant

$$s = \sigma_{xx} + \sigma_{yy} + \sigma_{zz} \tag{2.4}$$

of the stress tensor. Adding the two parts of ε_{ij} and introducing the Kronecker symbol δ_{ij} defined by

$$\delta_{ij} = \begin{cases} 1, & i = j, \\ 0, & i \neq j, \end{cases}$$

one may write

$$\varepsilon_{ij} = \frac{1}{2G}\left(\sigma_{ij} - \frac{\nu}{1+\nu}s\delta_{ij}\right) + \alpha\Theta\delta_{ij} \tag{2.5}$$

as the generalized Hooke's law.

Solving Equations (2.5) for the σ_{ij}, one obtains

$$\sigma_{ij} = 2G\left(\varepsilon_{ij} + \frac{\nu}{1-2\nu}e\delta_{ij} - \frac{1+\nu}{1-2\nu}\alpha\Theta\delta_{ij}\right). \tag{2.6}$$

The quantity

$$e = \varepsilon_{xx} + \varepsilon_{yy} + \varepsilon_{zz} \tag{2.7}$$

represents the first invariant of the strain tensor. We note the following relation between s and e, which may be obtained directly from either of Equations (2.5) or (2.6), as

$$e = \frac{1-2\nu}{1+\nu}\frac{s}{2G} + 3\alpha\Theta. \tag{2.8}$$

Using Equations (2.6) and (2.3), the elastic potential for an isotropic Hookean solid can now be written in the form

$$W = G\left\{\sum_i\sum_j \varepsilon_{ij}^2 + \frac{\nu}{1-2\nu}e^2 - \frac{2(1+\nu)}{1-2\nu}\alpha\Theta e\right\} + f(\Theta), \tag{2.9}$$

noting that

$$\frac{\partial e}{\partial \varepsilon_{ij}} = \delta_{ij}.$$

The function of integration $f(\Theta)$ will be determined in Chapter 5. It is of no importance in the present statement of linearized theory and may be dropped.

Thus far nothing has been said about the strain tensor ε_{ij} appearing in the preceding equations. Various definitions have been proposed† and are in use. However, if the deformations are small, all of these definitions reduce to the following relations between the components of strain ε_{ij} and the displacement vector u_i:

$$\varepsilon_{ij} = \frac{1}{2}\left(\frac{\partial u_i}{\partial j} + \frac{\partial u_j}{\partial i}\right) \qquad (i, j = x, y, z), \qquad (2.10)$$

or, explicitly, with $u_x = u$, $u_y = v$, $u_z = w$,

$$\left.\begin{array}{ll}
\varepsilon_{xx} = \dfrac{\partial u}{\partial x}, \qquad \varepsilon_{yy} = \dfrac{\partial v}{\partial y}, \qquad \varepsilon_{zz} = \dfrac{\partial w}{\partial z}, \\[2mm]
2\varepsilon_{xy} = 2\varepsilon_{yx} = \dfrac{\partial u}{\partial y} + \dfrac{\partial v}{\partial x}, \qquad 2\varepsilon_{yz} = 2\varepsilon_{zy} = \dfrac{\partial v}{\partial z} + \dfrac{\partial w}{\partial y}, \\[2mm]
2\varepsilon_{zx} = 2\varepsilon_{xz} = \dfrac{\partial w}{\partial x} + \dfrac{\partial u}{\partial z}.
\end{array}\right\} \qquad (2.10a)$$

Equations (2.10) are *kinematic relations* and, like Equation (2.1), are valid in any continuum irrespective of the material.

The set of basic equations of linear thermoelasticity is now complete. We have altogether fifteen equations, Equations (2.1), (2.3), and (2.10), for the fifteen unknown quantities σ_{ij}, ε_{ij}, and u_i. Since coupling between deformation and temperature is neglected here, the temperature Θ does not constitute an additional unknown as in the general case of thermoelasticity.

We note that the equations of linear thermoelasticity differ from those of isothermal elasticity only in the elastic potential W, i.e., in the stress-strain relations of Equations (2.5) or (2.6).

2.2. The Temperature Field

As pointed out in the previous discussion, the temperature distribution in the body may, in quasistatic thermoelasticity, be determined independently of the state of stress and strain which it produces. In fact, finding Θ always constitutes the first step in the solution of a thermoelastic problem. Consequently, a short review of the pertinent equations for a homogeneous body will be presented in this section.‡

---

† For a detailed discussion see [3], Chapter XI.
‡ A standard text in the analysis of heat conduction is the book by Carlslaw and Jaeger [4].

The amount of heat q flowing per unit time through a surface element of unit area is proportional to the temperature gradient in the direction of the normal n of the element (Fourier's law),

$$q = -k \frac{\partial \Theta}{\partial n} . \qquad (2.11)$$

The factor of proportionality k is called the *thermal conductivity* of the material. The minus sign is due to the fact that heat flows in the direction of decreasing temperature.

If more heat flows into a body than flows out of it, heat will be stored and the temperature of the body will rise. The same is true if heat is produced within the body by heat sources. By setting up the heat balance for an element of a body, one arrives at the following fundamental equation

$$\frac{\partial \Theta}{\partial t} = a\nabla^2\Theta + \frac{S}{c\rho} . \qquad (2.12)$$

The specific heat c is the amount of heat necessary to raise the temperature of a unit mass by one degree. The coefficient a is determined by the relation

$$a = \frac{k}{c\rho} , \qquad (2.13)$$

where ρ is the mass density. The Laplacian operator ∇^2 is given in cartesian coordinates (x, y, z) as

$$\nabla^2 = \frac{\partial^2}{\partial x^2} + \frac{\partial^2}{\partial y^2} + \frac{\partial^2}{\partial z^2} , \qquad (2.14)$$

and in cylindrical coordinates (r, θ, z) as

$$\nabla^2 = \frac{\partial^2}{\partial r^2} + \frac{1}{r}\frac{\partial}{\partial r} + \frac{1}{r^2}\frac{\partial^2}{\partial \theta^2} + \frac{\partial^2}{\partial z^2} . \qquad (2.15)$$

The symbol S in Equation (2.12) represents the strength of the heat source distribution. It is equal to the amount of heat produced within the body per unit volume per unit time.

For a *stationary* (time-independent) and source-free temperature field, Equation (2.12) reduces to

$$\nabla^2\Theta = 0. \qquad (2.16)$$

To complete the statement of Equation (2.12), the appropriate initial and boundary conditions must be prescribed. The initial condition specifies the temperature distribution in the body at time $t = 0$ while the boundary condition determines the transfer of heat between the body and the surrounding medium at all times $t > 0$. In the simplest case, the temperature T_s

of the surface is prescribed as a function of space and time. Although this case is frequently used on account of its mathematical simplicity, it rarely occurs in physical reality. A more realistic (but mathematically more complicated) boundary condition would prescribe the temperature T of the surrounding medium and the law of heat transfer to the body. A linearized version of this law is known as *Newton's law of heat transfer* and is given by

$$k\left(\frac{\partial \Theta}{\partial n}\right)_s = \lambda(T - T_s),\tag{2.17}$$

where $T - T_s$ is the temperature difference between the surface of the body and the surrounding medium, and λ is the coefficient of heat transfer.

As an example for a stationary temperature distribution consider a *cylindrical tube* of inner radius a and outer radius b. Inner and outer surfaces are kept at constant uniform temperature T_a and T_b, respectively. The plane end surfaces are perfectly insulated to prevent loss of heat. We wish to find the steady-state temperature distribution in the tube.

Because of rotational symmetry and absence of heat flow in the axial direction, temperature will be a function of the radial distance r only, $\Theta = \Theta(r)$. By taking Equation (2.15) into account, Equation (2.16) becomes

$$\frac{d^2\Theta}{dr^2} + \frac{1}{r}\frac{d\Theta}{dr} \equiv \frac{1}{r}\frac{d}{dr}\left(r\frac{d\Theta}{dr}\right) = 0,$$

or

$$\frac{d\Theta}{dr} = \frac{C_1}{r},$$

which has the solution

$$\Theta = C_1(\log r + C_2).$$

The integration constants C_1 and C_2 are determined from the boundary conditions

$$T_0 + \Theta = T_a \quad \text{in} \quad r = a,$$

$$T_0 + \Theta = T_b \quad \text{in} \quad r = b,$$

where T_0 is the uniform reference temperature. With $T_a - T_0 = \Theta_a$ and $T_b - T_0 = \Theta_b$, the constants are

$$C_2 = \frac{\Theta_a \log b - \Theta_b \log a}{\Theta_b - \Theta_a}, \qquad C_1 = \frac{\Theta_b - \Theta_a}{\log b/a},$$

and the solution finally becomes,

$$\Theta = \frac{1}{\log b/a}\left(\Theta_a \log \frac{b}{r} + \Theta_b \log \frac{r}{a}\right).\tag{2.18}$$

As an example for a nonstationary case consider an *instantaneous point source* of heat in an infinite body. At time $t = 0$, a quantity of heat Q is deposited at the origin producing a discontinuous jump in the temperature at this point. Immediately afterwards the heat will spread out into the body and the temperature at the origin will decrease while all other points will first experience an increase and later a decrease in temperature. After a sufficiently long time, the body will return to its initial temperature.

The temperature field will have point symmetry (spherical symmetry) with respect to the origin. Writing $R^2 = x^2 + y^2 + z^2$, we have

$$\frac{\partial \Theta}{\partial j} = \frac{\partial \Theta}{\partial R}\frac{\partial R}{\partial j} = \frac{j}{R}\frac{\partial \Theta}{\partial R}, \qquad \frac{\partial^2 \Theta}{\partial j^2} = \frac{\partial}{\partial j}\left(\frac{j}{R}\frac{\partial \Theta}{\partial R}\right) = \frac{j^2}{R^2}\frac{\partial^2 \Theta}{\partial R^2} + \frac{R^2 - j^2}{R^3}\frac{\partial \Theta}{\partial R}$$

$$\text{for} \quad j = x, y, z\,.$$

Hence, Equation (2.14) may be written as

$$\nabla^2 \Theta = \sum_j \frac{\partial^2 \Theta}{\partial j^2} = \frac{\partial^2 \Theta}{\partial R^2} + \frac{2}{R}\frac{\partial \Theta}{\partial R} \equiv \frac{1}{R^2}\frac{\partial}{\partial R}\left(R^2 \frac{\partial \Theta}{\partial R}\right). \tag{2.19}$$

The equation of heat conduction, Equation (2.12), now reads

$$\frac{\partial \Theta}{\partial t} = \frac{a}{R^2}\frac{\partial}{\partial R}\left(R^2 \frac{\partial \Theta}{\partial R}\right). \tag{2.20}$$

Since there are no heat sources outside of the origin, the second term on the right-hand side of Equation (2.12) vanishes here.

Application of the Laplace transform†

$$f^*(s) = \int_0^\infty f(t)e^{-st}\,dt$$

to Equation (2.20) with the initial condition $\Theta(0) = 0$ yields

$$s\Theta^* = \frac{a}{R^2}\frac{d}{dR}\left(R^2 \frac{d\Theta^*}{dR}\right).$$

The temperature Θ and its transform Θ^* must remain bounded as $R \to \infty$. This eliminates one of the two solutions of the above equation leaving

$$\Theta^* = \frac{A}{R}e^{-R\sqrt{s/a}},$$

where A is a constant of integration.

---

† For an introductory text on the theory of the Laplace transform the reader is referred to [5].

At all times $t > 0$, the amount of heat contained in the infinite body remains unchanged and equal to the heat Q supplied initially at the origin. The heat necessary to raise the temperature of the volume dV by one degree is $\rho c dV$; consequently, with $dV = 4\pi R^2 dR$,

$$Q = \int_0^\infty \rho c \Theta 4\pi R^2 \, dR \, .$$

Taking the Laplace transform of both sides, one finds

$$\frac{Q}{s} = 4\pi\rho c \int_0^\infty \Theta^* R^2 \, dR = 4\pi\rho c A \int_0^\infty e^{-R\sqrt{s/a}} R \, dR = 4\pi\rho c A \frac{a}{s} \, .$$

This determines the constant A and the transformed solution is

$$\Theta^* = \frac{1}{4\pi a} \frac{Q}{\rho c} \frac{1}{R} e^{-R\sqrt{s/a}} \, .$$

A table of transforms† may be used for the inversion of this expression. One finds

$$\Theta = \frac{1}{(4\pi a t)^{3/2}} \frac{Q}{\rho c} e^{-R^2/4at} \, . \tag{2.21}$$

We note that immediately after application of the heat source, $t \to 0$, the temperature change is still zero at every point in the body with the exception of the origin $R = 0$ where it is infinite. After a sufficiently long time, $t \to \infty$, the body resumes its initial temperature $\Theta = 0$.

2.3.   Stress-Free Temperature Fields

It has already been indicated that if a body is free to expand, a uniform temperature change does not produce any stresses. Now, we wish to find the most general conditions which must be satisfied by a temperature field so that no stresses are produced by the field.

From Equations (2.5) we have, with $\sigma_{ij} = 0$,

$$\varepsilon_{xx} = \varepsilon_{yy} = \varepsilon_{zz} = \alpha\Theta \, , \qquad \varepsilon_{xy} = \varepsilon_{yz} = \varepsilon_{zx} = 0 \, .$$

The six components of strain ε_{ij} are not independent since they are functions of the three components u_i of the displacement vector, Equations (2.10).

---

† A very comprehensive collection of Laplace transforms is available in [6]. The transform needed here is given on p. 245.

Six relations, known as *compatibility conditions*,† exist between the ε_{ij} and may be obtained by eliminating the u_i from Equations (2.10a). For instance, one has

$$\frac{\partial^2 \varepsilon_{xx}}{\partial y^2} = \frac{\partial^3 u}{\partial y^2 \partial x}, \qquad \frac{\partial^2 \varepsilon_{yy}}{\partial x^2} = \frac{\partial^3 v}{\partial x^2 \partial y}, \qquad 2\frac{\partial^2 \varepsilon_{xy}}{\partial x \partial y} = \frac{\partial^3 u}{\partial x \partial y^2} + \frac{\partial^3 v}{\partial x^2 \partial y}.$$

This gives the first of the six relations (2.22). The others are obtained in a similar manner.

$$\frac{\partial^2 \varepsilon_{xx}}{\partial y^2} + \frac{\partial^2 \varepsilon_{yy}}{\partial x^2} = 2\frac{\partial^2 \varepsilon_{xy}}{\partial x \partial y}, \qquad \frac{\partial^2 \varepsilon_{xx}}{\partial y \partial z} = \frac{\partial}{\partial x}\left(-\frac{\partial \varepsilon_{yz}}{\partial x} + \frac{\partial \varepsilon_{zx}}{\partial y} + \frac{\partial \varepsilon_{xy}}{\partial z}\right), \quad (2.22)$$

and so on, by cyclic permutation of indices. Substitution of the values of ε_{ij} from above into Equations (2.22) gives us

$$\frac{\partial^2(\alpha\Theta)}{\partial x^2} + \frac{\partial^2(\alpha\Theta)}{\partial y^2} = 0, \qquad \frac{\partial^2(\alpha\Theta)}{\partial y^2} + \frac{\partial^2(\alpha\Theta)}{\partial z^2} = 0, \qquad \frac{\partial^2(\alpha\Theta)}{\partial z^2} + \frac{\partial^2(\alpha\Theta)}{\partial x^2} = 0,$$

and hence

$$\frac{\partial^2(\alpha\Theta)}{\partial x^2} = \frac{\partial^2(\alpha\Theta)}{\partial y^2} = \frac{\partial^2(\alpha\Theta)}{\partial z^2} = 0.$$

Also,

$$\frac{\partial^2(\alpha\Theta)}{\partial x \partial y} = 0, \qquad \frac{\partial^2(\alpha\Theta)}{\partial y \partial z} = 0, \qquad \frac{\partial^2(\alpha\Theta)}{\partial z \partial x} = 0.$$

The six equations in $\alpha\Theta$ have as their only solution

$$\alpha\Theta = a_0 + a_1 x + a_2 y + a_3 z, \qquad (2.23)$$

where $a_0, \ldots, a_3$ are arbitrary functions of time.

For the homogeneous body where $\alpha = $ const., substitution of Equation (2.23) into Equation (2.12) gives

$$\frac{\partial \Theta}{\partial t} = \frac{S}{c\rho}.$$

Since Θ is a linear function of space coordinates, this condition will be satisfied if one or the other of the following conditions is fulfilled:

(a) No heat sources are present ($S = 0$) and coefficients $a_0, \ldots, a_3$ are constants; the temperature field is then stationary.

(b) Heat sources are linearly distributed over the body; the coefficients $a_0, \ldots, a_3$ are then functions of time.

† See reference [1], p. 28.

Equations (2.22) are necessary for compatibility, but they are not sufficient except for a simply connected body. In a multiply connected body (i.e., a body with cavities) additional conditions have to be satisfied.† The deformations due to the temperature field of Equation (2.23) satisfy these conditions.‡

In conclusion, therefore, we may state that in a body which is free to expand on its surface and free of heat sources, the necessary and sufficient conditions for a stress-free temperature field are that it is stationary and linearly dependent on the space coordinates.

2.4. Methods of Solution. Thermoelastic Potential

Due to the linearity of the basic equations (2.1), (2.6), and (2.10), it is possible to eliminate certain unknowns and obtain equations containing either the displacement components u_i or the stress components σ_{ij} only. This will be left as an exercise. The first case results in three equations known as the *generalized Navier equations*:

$$\nabla^2 u_i + \frac{1}{1-2\nu}\frac{\partial e}{\partial i} = \frac{2(1+\nu)}{1-2\nu}\alpha\frac{\partial\Theta}{\partial i}, \qquad (2.24)$$

where

$$e = \sum_i \frac{\partial u_i}{\partial i}.$$

In the second case, we obtain the six *generalized Beltrami-Michell equations*:

$$(1+\nu)\nabla^2\sigma_{ij} + \frac{\partial^2 s}{\partial i\partial j} = -E\alpha\left(\frac{\partial^2\Theta}{\partial i\partial j} + \frac{1+\nu}{1-\nu}\nabla^2\Theta\delta_{ij}\right), \qquad (2.25)$$

with

$$E = 2(1+\nu)G$$

as Young's modulus. Letting $j = i$ and summing, one gets

$$\nabla^2 s = -\frac{2E\alpha}{1-\nu}\nabla^2\Theta. \qquad (2.26)$$

It therefore follows that $\nabla^2 s = 0$ when a stationary temperature field with no heat sources exists in the body.

To ensure that each solution of Equations (2.25) is "statically admissible," we know that Equations (2.1) must also be satisfied.

---

† [7], p. 92.
‡ [7], p. 95.

Equations (2.24) and (2.25) are linear, nonhomogeneous equations. Because of this linearity, the principle of superposition is valid, and the general solution may be separated into two parts: a particular solution $\bar{u}_i$ of the nonhomogeneous equation, and the general solution $\bar{\bar{u}}_i$ of the homogeneous equation for which $\Theta = 0$. It is important to note that once a particular solution $\bar{u}_i$ is known, linear thermoelasticity is reduced to isothermal elasticity.

A convenient method of finding a particular solution $\bar{u}_i$ of Equations (2.24) is provided by introducing the *thermoelastic potential* Φ, writing

$$\bar{u}_i = \frac{\partial \Phi}{\partial i}. \qquad (2.27)$$

Substitution of this expression into Equations (2.24) yields the relation

$$\nabla^2 \Phi = \frac{1 + \nu}{1 - \nu} \alpha \Theta. \qquad (2.28)$$

Since, in general, the particular solution may be chosen independent of the boundary conditions of the problem, any particular solution which results from Equation (2.28) is applicable. For a nonstationary, source-free temperature distribution a solution of this equation is given by

$$\Phi = \frac{1 + \nu}{1 - \nu} \alpha a \int_0^t \Theta \, dt + \Phi_0 + t\Phi_1, \qquad (2.29)$$

where $\nabla^2 \Phi_1 = 0$ and $\Phi_0 = \Phi(t = 0)$ represents the initial thermoelastic potential. The solution may easily be verified by substituting it into Equation (2.28) and utilizing Equation (2.12) with $S = 0$.

The solution $\bar{\bar{u}}_i$ of the homogeneous equation

$$\nabla^2 u_i + \frac{1}{1 - 2\nu} \frac{\partial e}{\partial i} = 0 \qquad (2.30)$$

must be adjusted in such a manner that the sum $u_i = \bar{u}_i + \bar{\bar{u}}_i$ satisfies the prescribed boundary conditions.

It is well known from isothermal elasticity that, in spite of their simple appearance, the treatment of Equations (2.30) is not very convenient. The same is true for Equations (2.25). For that reason, the $\bar{\bar{u}}_i$ are usually expressed in terms of certain so-called *displacement functions*. Of course, if any advantage is to be realized over Equations (2.30), these functions should belong to a well-studied and mathematically simple class. Two methods are in use. The first employs harmonic functions ψ (i.e., functions that are solutions of the Laplace equation $\nabla^2 \psi = 0$) and is known as the

Neuber-Papkovich representation:

$$\bar{\bar{u}}_i = 4(1 - \nu)\psi_i - \frac{\partial \Psi}{\partial i}, \qquad (i = x, y, z) \tag{2.31}$$

where

$$\Psi = \sum_i i\psi_i + \psi_0, \qquad \nabla^2\psi_i = 0, \qquad \nabla^2\psi_0 = 0. \tag{2.32}$$

The method involves four independent harmonic functions ψ_i and ψ_0. Frequently, one of the four functions, for example ψ_0, may be dropped.[†] It has been proved[‡] that any solution to Equations (2.30) may be written in the form of Equations (2.31).

The second method is due to *Galerkin* and *Westergaard*. It makes use of biharmonic functions χ (solutions of the biharmonic equation $\nabla^2\nabla^2\chi = 0$) and represents $\bar{\bar{u}}_i$ in the form

$$\bar{\bar{u}}_i = 2(1 - \nu)\nabla^2\chi_i - \sum_j \frac{\partial^2\chi_j}{\partial i \partial j}, \qquad (i, j = x, y, z) \tag{2.33}$$

with

$$\nabla^2\nabla^2\chi_i = 0,$$

which contains three biharmonic functions χ_i. It is well known that every biharmonic function can be expressed in terms of two harmonic functions. Since only four harmonic functions appear in Equations (2.31), it follows that two of the six harmonic functions involved in Equations (2.33) are not independent.

Noting that

$$e = \nabla^2\Phi + (1 - 2\nu)\nabla^2\Psi,$$

the stresses corresponding to Equations (2.27) and (2.31),

$$\sigma_{ij} = 2G\left[\frac{\partial^2(\Phi - \Psi)}{\partial i \partial j} + (\nu\nabla^2\Psi - \nabla^2\Phi)\delta_{ij} + 2(1 - \nu)\left(\frac{\partial\psi_i}{\partial j} + \frac{\partial\psi_j}{\partial i}\right)\right] \tag{2.34}$$

follow from Equations (2.6) and (2.10). Similarly, upon combining Equations (2.27) and (2.33), the stresses are given by

$$\sigma_{ij} = 2G\left[\frac{\partial^2(\Phi - \Omega)}{\partial i \partial j} + (\nu\nabla^2\Omega - \nabla^2\Phi)\delta_{ij} + (1 - \nu)\left(\frac{\partial\chi_i}{\partial j} + \frac{\partial\chi_j}{\partial i}\right)\right], \tag{2.35}$$

for which

$$\Omega = \sum_i \frac{\partial\chi_i}{\partial i}.$$

---

† See reference [8].
‡ See reference [9].

2.5. Boundary Conditions. Uniqueness

The system of fundamental equations, Equations (2.1), (2.3), and (2.10), has to be complemented by boundary conditions, i.e., conditions on the surface of the body. Assuming the temperature field to be known, these conditions may be divided into three groups.

In the *first boundary value problem*, the forces acting on the surface of the body are prescribed. Let **f** be the prescribed force vector with components f_i, and let **n**, with components n_i, be the unit normal vector of the surface, pointing outwards. Then, the stress vector **p** on the surface with components†
$p_i = \sum_j \sigma_{ij} n_j$ must be equal to **f**:

$$f_i = \sum_j \sigma_{ij} n_j \qquad (i, j = x, y, z). \tag{2.36}$$

In the *second boundary value problem*, the displacements u_i of the points on the surface of the body are prescribed. In the *third boundary value problem* (or mixed problem), the forces are prescribed over one part, and the displacements are prescribed over the remaining part of the surface of the body.

The static or quasistatic problem thus stated has a unique solution provided the possibility of discontinuities in displacements and stresses is taken into account. This has been proved by Boley and Weiner‡ for the homogeneous isotropic body.

2.6. Example: Instantaneous Point Source

The quasistatic stresses in an infinite body produced by an instantaneous point source, Equation (2.21), are to be determined.

Substituting Equation (2.21) into Equation (2.29) and performing the integration, we get

$$\Phi = \frac{K}{2GR}\left[1 - \mathrm{erf}\left(\frac{R}{2\sqrt{at}}\right)\right] + \Phi_0 + t\Phi_1,$$

where the error function is defined by

$$\mathrm{erf}(u) = \frac{2}{\sqrt{\pi}} \int_0^u e^{-u^2}\, du,$$

and

$$K = \frac{1+\nu}{1-\nu}\frac{\alpha G}{2\pi}\frac{Q}{\rho c}.$$

---

† See reference [1], p. 39. See also Equation (5.16).
‡ See reference [7].

After a sufficiently long time, $t \to \infty$, displacements and stresses will return to zero. This condition will be satisfied if we let

$$\Phi_0 = - \frac{K}{2GR}, \qquad \Phi_1 = 0.$$

Hence,

$$\Phi = - \frac{K}{2G} \frac{1}{R} \operatorname{erf}\left(\frac{R}{2\sqrt{at}}\right). \tag{2.37}$$

The corresponding stresses are from Equation (2.34),

$$\sigma_{xx} = 2G\left(\frac{\partial^2 \Phi}{\partial x^2} - \nabla^2\Phi\right) = \frac{K}{R^2}\Bigg\{ \left(1 - \frac{3x^2}{R^2}\right)\left[\frac{1}{R}\operatorname{erf}\left(\frac{R}{2\sqrt{at}}\right) - \frac{1}{\sqrt{\pi at}}e^{-R^2/4at}\right]$$

$$+ \frac{1}{2\sqrt{\pi}(at)^{3/2}}(x^2 - R^2)e^{-R^2/4at}\Bigg\}, \tag{2.38}$$

and two similar equations for σ_{yy} and σ_{zz}. Also,

$$\sigma_{xy} = 2G\frac{\partial^2 \Phi}{\partial x \partial y} = \frac{3K}{R^4} xy\left[\frac{1}{\sqrt{\pi at}}\left(1 + \frac{R^2}{6at}\right)e^{-R^2/4at} - \frac{1}{R}\operatorname{erf}\left(\frac{R}{2\sqrt{at}}\right)\right], \tag{2.39}$$

with similar equations for σ_{yz} and σ_{zx}.

All stresses and displacements vanish at infinity. In addition, the radial displacement $u = \partial\Phi/\partial R$ is zero at the origin. Hence, all initial and boundary conditions are satisfied and the preceding equations represent the solution of the problem.

2.7. Axisymmetrical Problems with Shearing Stresses Vanishing in a Plane

Suppose that the problem, besides exhibiting symmetry about the z-axis, is such that the plane $z = 0$ is free of applied shearing stress. In that case, the solution may be represented in terms of a single harmonic function.†
Letting

$$\psi_0 = -(1 - 2\nu)\varphi, \qquad \psi_x = \psi_y = 0, \qquad \psi_z = -\partial\varphi/\partial z$$

---

† See reference [2].

in Equations (2.31) and (2.32) and transforming to cylindrical coordinates r, θ, z, one obtains

$$
\left.
\begin{aligned}
u &= \frac{\partial \Phi}{\partial r} + (1 - 2v)\frac{\partial \varphi}{\partial r} + z\frac{\partial^2 \varphi}{\partial r \partial z}, \\
w &= \frac{\partial \Phi}{\partial z} - 2(1 - v)\frac{\partial \varphi}{\partial z} + z\frac{\partial^2 \varphi}{\partial z^2},
\end{aligned}
\right\}
\tag{2.40}
$$

$$
\left.
\begin{aligned}
\sigma_{rr} &= 2G\left(\frac{\partial^2 \Phi}{\partial r^2} - \nabla^2 \Phi + z\frac{\partial^3 \varphi}{\partial r^2 \partial z} + \frac{\partial^2 \varphi}{\partial r^2} + \frac{2v}{r}\frac{\partial \varphi}{\partial r}\right), \\
\sigma_{\theta\theta} &= 2G\left(\frac{1}{r}\frac{\partial \Phi}{\partial r} - \nabla^2 \Phi - \frac{z}{r}\frac{\partial^2 \varphi}{\partial r \partial z} - \frac{1}{r}\frac{\partial \varphi}{\partial r} - 2v\frac{\partial^2 \varphi}{\partial r^2}\right), \\
\sigma_{zz} &= 2G\left(\frac{\partial^2 \Phi}{\partial z^2} - \nabla^2 \Phi + z\frac{\partial^3 \varphi}{\partial z^3} - \frac{\partial^2 \varphi}{\partial z^2}\right), \\
\sigma_{rz} &= 2G\left(\frac{\partial^2 \Phi}{\partial r \partial z} + z\frac{\partial^3 \varphi}{\partial r \partial z^2}\right),
\end{aligned}
\right\}
\tag{2.41}
$$

where

$$
\nabla^2 \varphi \equiv \frac{\partial^2 \varphi}{\partial r^2} + \frac{1}{r}\frac{\partial \varphi}{\partial r} + \frac{\partial^2 \varphi}{\partial z^2} = 0.
\tag{2.42}
$$

As an example, consider a *stationary point source of heat* on the surface of the semi-infinite body $z \geqslant 0$. The surface is insulated against loss of heat and is free of applied stress. All stresses are to vanish at infinity.

The temperature field due to the point source, which satisfies the boundary condition $\partial \Theta / \partial z = 0$ on $z = 0$, is given by†

$$
\Theta(r, z) = \frac{M}{4\pi a \rho c}\frac{1}{R},
\tag{2.43}
$$

where M is the strength of the source, i.e., the amount of heat produced per unit time, and $R = \sqrt{r^2 + z^2}$. Using Equation (2.19), we may write Equation (2.28) in the form

$$
\frac{d}{dR}\left(R^2 \frac{d\Phi}{dR}\right) = KR,
$$

where

$$
K = \frac{1 + v}{1 - v}\frac{\alpha M}{4\pi a \rho c}.
$$

---

† See Problem 2 to follow.

A particular solution is

$$\Phi = \frac{K}{2} R,$$

with stresses from Equation (2.41),

$$\bar{\sigma}_{rz} = 2G \frac{\partial^2 \Phi}{\partial r \partial z} = -GK \frac{rz}{R^3},$$

$$\bar{\sigma}_{zz} = 2G\left(\frac{\partial^2 \Phi}{\partial z^2} - \nabla^2 \Phi\right) = GK\left(\frac{r^2}{R^3} - \frac{2}{R}\right).$$

All stresses vanish at infinity. At $z = 0$, the shearing stress is zero, but a normal stress $\bar{\sigma}_{zz} = -GK/r$ remains. To remove it, a second stress field $\bar{\bar{\sigma}}_{ij}$ corresponding to a harmonic function $\varphi(r, z)$ has to be superposed.

Let

$$\varphi(r, z) = A[z \log (z + R) - R].$$

Utilizing Equation (2.42), we prove that $\nabla^2 \varphi = 0$. Substituting into the third of Equations (2.41), we obtain

$$\bar{\bar{\sigma}}_{zz} = 2G\left(z \frac{\partial^3 \varphi}{\partial z^3} - \frac{\partial^2 \varphi}{\partial z^2}\right) = -2GA\left(\frac{1}{R} + \frac{z^2}{R^3}\right).$$

At $z = 0$, we must have $\sigma_{zz} = \bar{\sigma}_{zz} + \bar{\bar{\sigma}}_{zz} = 0$. This gives $A = -K/2$. Equations (2.40) and (2.41) now finally give

$$\left. \begin{array}{ll} u = (1 - v)K \dfrac{r}{R + z}, & w = (1 - v)K \log (R + z), \\[2mm] \sigma_{rr} = -2(1 - v) \dfrac{GK}{R + z}, & \sigma_{\theta\theta} = 2(1 - v)GK\left(\dfrac{1}{R + z} - \dfrac{1}{R}\right), \\[2mm] \multicolumn{2}{c}{\sigma_{zz} = \sigma_{rz} = 0.} \end{array} \right\} \quad (2.44)$$

In closing, we note without proof a result obtained by Sternberg and McDowell[†] for the general case of the semi-infinite body $z \geqslant 0$ with stress-free surface and arbitrarily prescribed axisymmetric surface temperature $\Theta(r, 0)$. They find the following expression for the two functions Φ and φ:

$$\Phi = -z \frac{\partial \varphi}{\partial z} + \varphi, \qquad \varphi = \frac{1 + v}{1 - v} \frac{\alpha}{4\pi} \int_0^{2\pi} d\omega \int_0^\infty \Theta(\rho, 0) \log (R + z)\rho \, d\rho,$$

$$(2.45)$$

where

$$R = [r^2 + z^2 + \rho^2 - 2r\rho \cos \omega]^{1/2}.$$

† See reference [11].

2.8. Green's Function I

A technique frequently used in isothermal elasticity is known as *Betti's method*.[†] It has been extended to thermoelasticity by V. M. Maysel[‡] who derived the formula

$$u_i(P) = \alpha \int_V \Theta(Q)\bar{s}(Q, P)\, dV(Q). \qquad (2.46)$$

The function $u_i(P)$ is the (static or quasistatic) displacement in the direction i at an arbitrary point P in a body due to the temperature field $\Theta(Q)$. The quantity $\bar{s} = \bar{\sigma}_{xx} + \bar{\sigma}_{yy} + \bar{\sigma}_{zz}$ is the sum of the normal stresses at point Q produced by a concentrated unit force acting at point P in the direction i.

To prove Equation (2.46), we proceed as follows. Let the body be at uniform initial temperature $\Theta \equiv 0$. Let part S_1 of its surface S be free of external loads with displacements being prescribed on the remaining part S_2 of S. Apply a force F of unit magnitude in the direction i at point P. This force will create stresses $\bar{\sigma}_{ij}$ and strains $\bar{\varepsilon}_{ij}$. Now, let the temperature of the body change from $\Theta = 0$ to $\Theta(Q)$. Thermal stresses σ_{ij} and thermal strains ε_{ij} will be produced and, as a consequence, point P will experience the displacement $u_i(P)$.

Since dynamic effects are neglected, the work done in this process by the external force F and the internal stresses $\bar{\sigma}_{ij}$ vanishes according to the principle of rate of work,[§] i.e.,

$$Fu_i(P) = \int_V \sum_i \sum_j \bar{\sigma}_{ij}\varepsilon_{ij}\, dV.$$

Reactions which may appear on the part S_2 of the surface will do no work since the displacements of their points of application vanish. If, now, the thermal strains ε_{ij} are expressed in terms of the thermal stresses σ_{ij}, and the nonthermal stresses $\bar{\sigma}_{ij}$ in terms of the corresponding strains $\bar{\varepsilon}_{ij}$ by means of Hooke's law, Equations (2.5) and (2.6), we obtain, letting $F = 1$,

$$u_i(P) = \int_V \sum_i \sum_j \sigma_{ij}\bar{\varepsilon}_{ij}\, dV + \int_V \alpha\Theta\bar{s}\, dV.$$

The thermal stress system σ_{ij} and the corresponding reactions on the surface of the body are self-equilibrating. By the principle of virtual displacements, the work done by such a system on any small deformation which is "kinematically admissible" is zero. Obviously, the deformation corresponding to the strains $\bar{\varepsilon}_{ij}$ satisfies this condition. Therefore, the first integral in the equation above vanishes, and this proves Equation (2.46).

---

† See reference [1], p. 354.
‡ A short account of Maysel's work may be found in [10]. The proof presented here is different from the one given there.
§ See, for instance, [1], Equation (26.5).

It frequently happens that the problem under consideration exhibits certain properties of symmetry. Consider, for instance, a sphere under the action of a temperature field symmetric with respect to the center of the sphere. If Equation (2.46) is to be used for the radial displacement $u(r)$, a single unit force would have to be applied in the radial direction at a distance r from the center. Since symmetry would be lost in this method, an unnecessarily complicated procedure would result. However, a slight modification of Equation (2.46) removes this difficulty. Instead of a single load, let unit radial stresses f, uniformly distributed over the surface of a sphere of radius r, be applied. The work done by these stresses on the radial displacement $u(r)$ is $4\pi r^2 f u(r)$. By an argument similar to the one given above, one then obtains, with $dV = 4\pi \rho^2 d\rho$,

$$u(r) = \frac{\alpha}{r^2} \int_0^\infty \Theta(\rho)\bar{s}(\rho, r)\rho^2 d\rho, \tag{2.47}$$

where $\bar{s}(\rho, r)$ is now the sum of the normal stresses at point ρ due to the action of the unit radial stresses distributed uniformly over the spherical surface of radius r.

2.9. Green's Function II

A different procedure makes use of temperature singularities (point sources and dipoles) rather than concentrated forces. We consider two cases.

CASE 1. Let the body at time $t = 0$ be at the initial temperature $\Lambda(x, y, z)$. For $t > 0$ its surface is kept at temperature $\Omega(x, y, z, t)$.

Green's function $\Theta'(P, Q, t - \tau)$ is then defined as the temperature at point $P(x, y, z)$ at time t produced by an instantaneous point source[†] of strength 1 appearing at point $Q(\xi, \eta, \zeta)$ at time τ, while the surface S of the body is kept at temperature $\Theta' = 0$. Thus, Θ' is that solution of Equation (2.12),

$$\frac{\partial \Theta'}{\partial t} = a\nabla^2\Theta' \tag{2.48}$$

with the boundary condition

$$\Theta' = 0 \qquad \text{on } S, \tag{2.49}$$

which, for $t \to \tau$, exhibits a singularity at point $P = Q$ of the form [see Equation (2.21)]

$$\frac{1}{8[\pi a(t - \tau)]^{3/2}} e^{-R^2/4a(t-\tau)}, \tag{2.50}$$

where $R = [(x - \xi)^2 + (y - \eta)^2 + (z - \zeta)^2]^{1/2}$.

---

† See p. 9.

CASE 2.   Let the body at time $t = 0$ be at the initial temperature $\Lambda(x, y, z)$. For $t > 0$ there is transfer of heat from the surrounding medium of temperature $\Omega(x, y, z, t)$ according to Newton's law, Equation (2.17).

Green's function is defined in precisely the same manner as in Case (1), with the exception of the boundary condition of Equation (2.49) which is now to be replaced by

$$\frac{\partial \Theta'}{\partial n} + \frac{\lambda}{k} \Theta' = 0 \qquad \text{on } S. \tag{2.51}$$

In both cases the temperature distribution in the body is given by†

$$\Theta(P, t) = \int_V \Theta'(P, Q, t - 0)\Lambda(Q) \, dV_Q$$

$$- a \int_0^t d\tau \oint_S \frac{\partial \Theta'(P, Q, t - \tau)}{\partial n_Q} \Omega(Q, \tau) \, dS_Q. \tag{2.52}$$

Note that $dV_Q = d\xi \, d\eta \, d\zeta$ and dS_Q are volume and surface element, respectively, with ξ, η, ζ as integration variables. As usual, $\partial/\partial n_Q$ means differentiation with respect to ξ, η, ζ in the direction of the surface normal, positive outwards. Green's function is symmetric:

$$\Theta'(Q, P, t - \tau) = \Theta'(P, Q, t - \tau).$$

The same relations hold for a two-dimensional temperature distribution $\Theta(x, y, t)$. However, the volume integral has to be replaced by an integral over the plane region, and the surface integral has to be replaced by a line integral along the boundary of that region. Instead of an expression such as Equation (2.50), one has now

$$\frac{1}{4\pi a(t - \tau)} e^{-R^2/4a(t-\tau)}, \tag{2.53}$$

with $R = [(x - \xi)^2 + (y - \eta)^2]^{1/2}$.

From the preceding it follows immediately that the *stress field* $\sigma_{ij}(P, t)$ due to the temperature distribution of Equation (2.52) may be obtained by superposing two fields σ'_{ij} and σ''_{ij}:

$$\sigma_{ij}(P, t) = \int_V \sigma'_{ij}(P, Q, t)\Lambda(Q) \, dV_Q - \int_0^t d\tau \oint_S \sigma''_{ij}(P, Q, t - \tau)\Omega(Q, \tau) \, dS_Q. \tag{2.54}$$

Here $\sigma'_{ij}(P, Q, t)$ represents the stress at the generic point $P(x, y, z)$ at time t, due to the temperature field $\Theta'(P, Q, t)$ discussed above and produced by an instantaneous point source of strength 1 appearing at time $t = 0$ at the

---

† See reference [4], p. 353.

interior point $Q(\xi, \eta, \zeta)$. The stress $\sigma''_{ij}(P, Q, t - \tau)$ is the stress at the same point P, due to a temperature field $\Theta''(P, Q, t - \tau)$, where

$$\Theta'' = a \frac{\partial \Theta'(P, Q, t - \tau)}{\partial n_Q}, \tag{2.55}$$

and Q is now a point on the surface of the body. Physically, Θ'' represents the temperature distribution at time t produced by an instantaneous dipole of strength a, appearing at time τ at the surface point Q. The axis of the dipole is in the direction of the surface normal n.

It should be noted that Equation (2.54) is valid for homogeneous kinematic and dynamic boundary conditions only.† The stress distribution due to nonhomogeneous conditions may be determined separately, and superposed.

• *Problems*

1. By eliminating σ_{ij} and ε_{ij} from the basic equations of thermoelasticity, Equations (2.1), (2.6), and (2.10), derive the generalized Navier equations (2.24).

HINT: Substitute Equation (2.6) into Equation (2.1) and use

$$\sum_j \frac{\partial e}{\partial j} \delta_{ij} = \frac{\partial e}{\partial i}.$$

Employ Equation (2.10) and note that

$$\sum_i \frac{\partial^2 u_i}{\partial j \partial i} = \frac{\partial e}{\partial j}.$$

2. Show that the steady-state temperature distribution due to a point source of constant strength M (heat produced per unit time) at the origin $R = 0$ of an infinite body is given by

$$\theta = \frac{A}{R}, \qquad A = \frac{M}{4\pi k}, \qquad R^2 = x^2 + y^2 + z^2.$$

HINT: In determining the constant of integration A, use the fact that, under stationary conditions, the flow of heat per unit time across a sphere of arbitrary radius R must be equal to M.

3. Derive the generalized Beltrami-Michell equations (2.25).

HINT: With the aid of Equation (2.10), transform Equation (2.24) into the form

$$(1 - 2\nu)\nabla^2 \varepsilon_{ij} + \frac{\partial^2 e}{\partial i \partial j} = 2(1 + \nu)\alpha \frac{\partial^2 \Theta}{\partial i \partial j}$$

and introduce Equations (2.5).

---

† That is, at each point of the surface either displacement or applied stress is zero.

4. Show by direct substitution that Equations (2.31) represent a solution of Equations (2.24).

5. Show by direct substitution that Equations (2.33) represent a solution of Equations (2.24).

6. Derive the Laplacian operator in cylindrical coordinates, that is, Equation (2.15), from Equation (2.14).

HINT: From $r = \sqrt{x^2 + y^2}$ and $\theta = \tan^{-1} y/x$ it follows $\partial r/\partial x = x/r$, $\partial r/\partial y = y/r$, $\partial\theta/\partial x = -y/r$, $\partial\theta/\partial y = x/r$. Hence

$$\frac{\partial^2}{\partial x^2} = \frac{x^2}{r^2}\frac{\partial^2}{\partial r^2} + \frac{y^2}{r^3}\frac{\partial}{\partial r}.$$

7. An infinite body contains a spherical inclusion of radius a. The coefficient of thermal expansion of the body is α, that of the inclusion is $\alpha + \eta$. The temperature of inclusion and body is raised uniformly from T_0 to $T_0 + \Theta$. Determine the stresses in the body.

HINT: The problem has point symmetry. If R is the distance from the center of the inclusion, Equation (2.28) reads

$$\nabla^2\Phi = \frac{1}{R^2}\frac{d}{dR}\left(R^2\frac{d\Phi}{dR}\right) = \begin{cases} \dfrac{1+\nu}{1-\nu}\,\eta\theta = K & \text{in} \quad R < a, \\[2mm] 0 & \text{in} \quad R > a. \end{cases}$$

Hence,

$$\frac{d\Phi}{dR} = \begin{cases} K\left(\dfrac{R}{3} + \dfrac{c_1}{R^2}\right) & \text{in} \quad R < a, \\[4mm] \dfrac{c_2}{R^2} & \text{in} \quad R > a. \end{cases}$$

Determine c_1 and c_2 from the condition $u = d\Phi/dR = 0$ in $R = 0$, and u continuous across $R = a$. It follows for $R > a$ that

$$\frac{d\Phi}{dR} = \frac{K}{3}\frac{a^3}{R^2}.$$

The stresses in the body follow from Hooke's law upon substituting $du/dR = -2Ka^3/3R^3$ for the radial strain, and $u/R = Ka^3/3R^3$ for the circumferential strain. All boundary conditions (at $R = 0$, $R = a$, and $R \to \infty$) are satisfied.

Two-Dimensional Problems

Two-dimensional problems constitute an important special class within the field of thermoelasticity. They fall into two distinct types: plane strain and plane stress. In contradistinction to general three-dimensional thermoelasticity, very powerful mathematical methods are available for the solution of these problems. They will be discussed in this chapter.

3.1. Plane Strain

Let z be the coordinate in the direction of the axis of a cylindrical body. If load and temperature are independent of z, and if the end surfaces $z =$ const. of the cylinder are kept fixed then $\varepsilon_{zz} = 0$ throughout the body and the cylinder is said to be in a state of *plane strain*. Displacements and stresses are then independent of z, and

$$\sigma_{zx} = \sigma_{zy} = 0$$

by symmetry with respect to any plane $z =$ const. The equations of equilibrium, Equations (2.1), then reduce to

$$\frac{\partial \sigma_{xx}}{\partial x} + \frac{\partial \sigma_{yx}}{\partial y} = 0, \qquad \frac{\partial \sigma_{xy}}{\partial x} + \frac{\partial \sigma_{yy}}{\partial y} = 0. \tag{3.1}$$

These equations are identically satisfied by setting

$$\sigma_{xx} = \frac{\partial^2 F}{\partial y^2}, \qquad \sigma_{xy} = \sigma_{yx} = -\frac{\partial^2 F}{\partial x \partial y}, \qquad \sigma_{yy} = \frac{\partial^2 F}{\partial x^2}. \tag{3.2}$$

The function F is known as *Airy's stress function*. We next express ε_{xx}, ε_{xy}, ε_{yy}

in terms of σ_{xx}, σ_{xy}, σ_{yy} by means of Hooke's law, Equation (2.5), which, with $\varepsilon_{zz} = 0$, now reads

$$
\left.\begin{aligned}
2G\varepsilon_{xx} &= \sigma_{xx} - \nu(\sigma_{xx} + \sigma_{yy}) + E\alpha\Theta, \\
2G\varepsilon_{yy} &= \sigma_{yy} - \nu(\sigma_{xx} + \sigma_{yy}) + E\alpha\Theta, \\
2G\varepsilon_{xy} &= \sigma_{xy}.
\end{aligned}\right\}
\tag{3.3}
$$

Substituting Equation (3.3) into the first† of the six compatibility relations, Equations (2.22), one obtains the following differential equation for F,

$$
\nabla^2\nabla^2 F = -2G\frac{1+\nu}{1-\nu}\alpha\nabla^2\Theta.
\tag{3.4}
$$

A particular solution $\bar{F}$ of this equation is again provided by Equation (2.28),

$$
\nabla^2\Phi = \frac{1+\nu}{1-\nu}\alpha\Theta, \qquad \bar{F} = -2G\Phi,
\tag{3.5}
$$

with stresses according to Equation (3.2),

$$
\bar{\sigma}_{xx} = -2G\frac{\partial^2\Phi}{\partial y^2}, \qquad \bar{\sigma}_{xy} = 2G\frac{\partial^2\Phi}{\partial x\partial y}, \qquad \bar{\sigma}_{yy} = -2G\frac{\partial^2\Phi}{\partial x^2}.
\tag{3.6}
$$

The preceding equations are special cases of the *Neuber-Papkovich representation*. Indeed, choosing the two harmonic functions ψ_x and ψ_y in Equation (2.31) as real and imaginary parts of a complex analytic function $\varphi(z)$, where‡ $z = x + iy$ and $i = \sqrt{-1}$,

$$
\varphi(z) = \psi_x(x, y) + i\psi_y(x, y),
\tag{3.7}
$$

and utilizing the Cauchy-Riemann equations of complex-function theory, one has

$$
\nabla^2\Psi = 4\frac{\partial\psi_x}{\partial x} = 4\frac{\partial\psi_y}{\partial y}, \qquad \frac{\partial\psi_x}{\partial y} = -\frac{\partial\psi_y}{\partial x}.
$$

Equation (2.34) then becomes

$$
\begin{aligned}
\sigma_{xx} &= 2G\left[\frac{\partial^2(\Phi - \Psi)}{\partial x^2} + \nu\nabla^2\Psi - \nabla^2\Phi + 2(1 - \nu)\left(\frac{\partial\psi_x}{\partial x} + \frac{\partial\psi_x}{\partial x}\right)\right] \\
&= 2G\frac{\partial^2(\Psi - \Phi)}{\partial y^2},
\end{aligned}
$$

† The remaining equations are identically satisfied.
‡ Since the functions considered here are independent of the axial coordinate z, there is no danger of confusion between this coordinate and the complex variable z.

$$\sigma_{xy} = 2G\left[\frac{\partial^2(\Phi - \Psi)}{\partial x \partial y} + 2(1 - \nu)\left(\frac{\partial \psi_x}{\partial y} + \frac{\partial \psi_y}{\partial x}\right)\right] = -2G\frac{\partial^2(\Psi - \Phi)}{\partial x \partial y},$$

$$\sigma_{yy} = 2G\left[\frac{\partial^2(\Phi - \Psi)}{\partial y^2} + \nu\nabla^2\Psi - \nabla^2\Phi + 2(1 - \nu)\left(\frac{\partial \psi_y}{\partial y} + \frac{\partial \psi_y}{\partial y}\right)\right]$$

$$= 2G\frac{\partial^2(\Psi - \Phi)}{\partial x^2}.$$

Thus, upon setting

$$F = 2G(\Psi - \Phi), \tag{3.8}$$

the equations become identical with Equations (3.2).

In terms of the complex function $\varphi(z)$ in Equation (3.7), the stress function Ψ reads

$$2\Psi = \bar{z}\varphi(z) + z\overline{\varphi(z)} + \chi(z) + \overline{\chi(z)}, \tag{3.9}$$

with

$$\nabla^2\Psi = 4\frac{\partial^2\Psi}{\partial z \partial \bar{z}} = 2[\varphi'(z) + \overline{\varphi'(z)}],$$

where a superimposed bar denotes the conjugate complex quantity. Here, $\chi(z)$ is an analytic function whose real part is ψ_0.

Observing that

$$\frac{\partial \Psi}{\partial x} = \frac{\partial \Psi}{\partial z} + \frac{\partial \Psi}{\partial \bar{z}}, \qquad \frac{\partial \Psi}{\partial y} = i\left(\frac{\partial \Psi}{\partial z} - \frac{\partial \Psi}{\partial \bar{z}}\right),$$

we may now combine Equations (3.2) into the two complex equations:

$$\left.\begin{aligned}\sigma_{xx} + \sigma_{yy} &= 4G[\varphi'(z) + \overline{\varphi'(z)} - \lambda\Theta],\\\sigma_{xx} - \sigma_{yy} + 2i\sigma_{xy} &= 2G\left(\frac{\partial^2\Phi}{\partial x^2} - \frac{\partial^2\Phi}{\partial y^2} + 2i\frac{\partial^2\Phi}{\partial x \partial y}\right) - 4G[\overline{z\varphi''(z)} + \overline{\chi''(z)}],\end{aligned}\right\} \tag{3.10}$$

where

$$\lambda = \frac{1 + \nu}{1 - \nu}\frac{\alpha}{2}. \tag{3.11}$$

Similarly, upon combining Equations (2.27) and (2.31) and writing $u_x = u$, $u_y = v$, we find

$$u + iv = \frac{\partial \Phi}{\partial x} + i\frac{\partial \Phi}{\partial y} + \kappa\varphi(z) - z\overline{\varphi'(z)} - \overline{\chi'(z)}, \tag{3.12}$$

where

$$\kappa = 3 - 4\nu. \tag{3.13}$$

For the axial stress σ_{zz} one obtains from Equation (2.34), with $\partial/\partial z \equiv 0$,

$$\sigma_{zz} = 2G(\nu\nabla^2\Psi - \nabla^2\Phi) = \nu\nabla^2 F - 2G(1 - \nu)\nabla^2\Phi,$$

or, using Equations (3.2) and (2.28),

$$\sigma_{zz} = \nu(\sigma_{xx} + \sigma_{yy}) - E\alpha\Theta. \tag{3.14}$$

We still have to formulate the boundary conditions. In the *first boundary value problem*, the applied stresses $X(s)$ and $Y(s)$ are prescribed on the

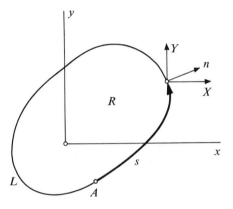

Figure 3.1

boundary L of the plane region R of Figure 3.1, where s is the arc length measured from some arbitrary point A. Then, from Equation (2.36) with $f_x = X, f_y = Y$, and with

$$n_x = \cos(n, x) = \frac{dy}{ds}, \qquad n_y = \cos(n, y) = -\frac{dx}{ds}, \qquad n_z = \cos(n, z) = 0,$$

one has the two boundary conditions

$$\sigma_{xx}\frac{dy}{ds} - \sigma_{xy}\frac{dx}{ds} = X(s),$$

$$\sigma_{yx}\frac{dy}{ds} - \sigma_{yy}\frac{dx}{ds} = Y(s).$$

Using Equations (3.2), this may be written

$$\left.\begin{aligned}
\frac{\partial^2 F}{\partial y^2}\frac{dy}{ds} + \frac{\partial^2 F}{\partial x \partial y}\frac{dx}{ds} &\equiv \frac{d}{ds}\left(\frac{\partial F}{\partial y}\right) = X(s), \\
\frac{\partial^2 F}{\partial x \partial y}\frac{dy}{ds} + \frac{\partial^2 F}{\partial x^2}\frac{dx}{ds} &\equiv \frac{d}{ds}\left(\frac{\partial F}{\partial x}\right) = -Y(s).
\end{aligned}\right\} \qquad (3.15)$$

Note that $\partial F/\partial x$ and $\partial F/\partial y$ are constant along those parts of the boundary which are free from external loads.

Equations (3.15) may be combined into the complex relation

$$\frac{d}{ds}\left(\frac{\partial F}{\partial x} + i\frac{\partial F}{\partial y}\right) = iX - Y,$$

or, upon integration,

$$\frac{\partial F}{\partial x} + i\frac{\partial F}{\partial y} = \int_0^s [iX(s) - Y(s)]\,ds + 2GC. \qquad (3.16)$$

The integration constant C may have different values on each contour of a multiply connected region. On one of these contours it can be chosen arbitrarily.

Substitution from Equations (3.8) and (3.9) leads to

$$\varphi(z) + z\overline{\varphi'(z)} + \overline{\chi'(z)} = \frac{\partial \Phi}{\partial x} + i\frac{\partial \Phi}{\partial y} + \frac{1}{2G}\int_0^s [iX(s) - Y(s)]\,ds + C. \qquad (3.17)$$

In the *second boundary value problem*, where the displacements u and v are prescribed along L Equation (3.12) furnishes the boundary condition

$$\kappa\varphi(z) - z\overline{\varphi'(z)} - \overline{\chi'(z)} = u + iv - \frac{\partial \Phi}{\partial x} - i\frac{\partial \Phi}{\partial y}. \qquad (3.18)$$

Due to the fact that u and v are not directly expressible in terms of the real stress function F, the formulation of the second boundary value problem in terms of F leads to rather complicated expressions. Thus, solutions are cumbersome if the real function approach is used. In the complex function formulation, however, no basic difference exists between first and second boundary value problems, as may be seen from a comparison of Equations (3.17) and (3.18).

In the *third boundary value problem*, Equation (3.17) will be valid over one part of the boundary, while Equation (3.18) will be valid over the remaining part.

3.2. Plane Stress

Consider a thin plate of thickness h. If the faces $z = \pm h/2$ are free of applied loads, and if the resultants of the forces on the lateral surface act in the mid-plane, the plate is said to be in a state of *plane stress*. The stress components σ_{zz}, σ_{xz}, and σ_{yz} are then very small. If they are neglected entirely, Hooke's law, Equation (2.5), reads,

$$\varepsilon_{xx} = \frac{1}{E}(\sigma_{xx} - \nu\sigma_{yy}) + \alpha\Theta, \qquad \varepsilon_{yy} = \frac{1}{E}(\sigma_{yy} - \nu\sigma_{xx}) + \alpha\Theta, \left.\begin{array}{}\\ \\ \\ \\\end{array}\right\}$$

$$\varepsilon_{xy} = \frac{\sigma_{xy}}{2G}.$$
(3.19)

In terms of the strain components the stresses are now

$$\sigma_{xx} = \frac{2G}{1-\nu}[\varepsilon_{xx} + \nu\varepsilon_{yy} - (1+\nu)\alpha\Theta], \left.\begin{array}{}\\ \\ \\ \\\end{array}\right\}$$

$$\sigma_{yy} = \frac{2G}{1-\nu}[\varepsilon_{yy} + \nu\varepsilon_{xx} - (1+\nu)\alpha\Theta].$$
(3.20)

Equations (3.1) remain valid in plane stress but, strictly speaking, stress and strain may now vary with z. Neglecting these variations, or taking mean values over the thickness of the plate, Airy's stress function $F(x, y)$ may again be introduced through Equations (3.2). However, using Equations (3.19), we find that F now satisfies, instead of Equation (3.4), the following differential equation:

$$\nabla^2\nabla^2 F = -E\alpha\nabla^2\Theta.$$
(3.21)

Equation (3.5) has, therefore, to be replaced by

$$\nabla^2\Phi = (1+\nu)\alpha\Theta.$$
(3.22)

All other equations remain true provided λ and κ, Equations (3.11) and (3.13), are replaced by

$$\lambda = \frac{1+\nu}{2}\alpha, \qquad \kappa = \frac{3-\nu}{1+\nu}.$$
(3.23)

In the preceding equations the temperature Θ is assumed to be constant across the thickness of the plate, $\Theta = \Theta(x, y)$. If this is not the case, the plate will, in general, not remain plane. (See Chapter 4.)

3.3. Method of Solution. Real Function Approach

The first step in obtaining a solution to a plane strain or plane stress problem consists in finding a solution of Equation (3.5) or of (3.22), as the case may be. This is usually a simple matter since, in solving these equations, no regard need be given to the boundary conditions. Once the thermoelastic potential Φ is known, there are two possibilities for continuing. One may either operate in the real function domain, i.e., use Equation (3.4) or (3.21), respectively, or one may use the complex function approach, Equation (3.9). We first discuss the real function method.†

In accordance with Equation (3.8), we write

$$F = 2G(\Psi - \Phi). \tag{3.24}$$

The stress function Ψ represents an isothermal problem and is a solution of

$$\nabla^2 \nabla^2 \Psi = 0. \tag{3.25}$$

By employing the principle of superposition, the two-dimensional biharmonic function Ψ may be constructed as a finite or infinite series of properly chosen biharmonic functions. In cartesian coordinates x, y, the following functions may be used,

$$e^{\pm \mu y} \cos \mu x, \qquad x e^{\pm \mu y} \cos \mu x, \qquad y e^{\pm \mu y} \cos \mu x, \tag{3.26}$$

where μ is an arbitrary constant. All other combinations obtained by interchanging x and y, and/or by replacing $\cos \mu x$ by $\sin \mu x$ are also biharmonic. In polar coordinates r, θ, a complete set of biharmonic functions, periodic in θ, is

$$\log r, \qquad r^2 \log r, \qquad r \log r \cos \theta, \qquad r^{\pm n} \cos n\theta,$$

$$r^{2 \pm n} \cos n\theta \qquad (n = 0, 1, 2, 3, \ldots), \tag{3.27}$$

and the corresponding expressions with $\cos n\theta$ replaced by $\sin n\theta$.

If full use is to be made of the functions of Equations (3.26) and (3.27) it will, in general, be necessary to express the boundary conditions in the form of Fourier series or Fourier integrals.

Of course, the Green's function method described in Section 2.8 may also be used in two-dimensional thermoelasticity. It is of particular value in those cases where the function $\bar{s}$ is already known from isothermal elasticity. If the problem exhibits symmetry about the z-axis, the following equation, analogous to Equation (2.47), may easily be derived:

$$u(r) = \frac{\alpha}{r} \int_0^\infty \Theta(\rho) \bar{s}(\rho, r) \rho \, d\rho. \tag{3.28}$$

Here, $\bar{s}(\rho, r)$ denotes the sum of the normal stresses at radius ρ due to the action of unit radial loading uniformly distributed over the circumference of the circle of radius r.

---

† For a concise review of this method as applied to isothermal elasticity, see reference [12], where an extensive list of references may be found. Applications to thermoelasticity are given in references [13] and [10].

3.4. Method of Solution. Complex Function Approach†

As in the preceding section, we suppose that the thermoelastic potential Φ has already been determined. The right-hand side of either Equation (3.17) or (3.18) is then a known function and the two boundary value problems may both be represented in the form

$$K\varphi(z) + z\overline{\varphi'(z)} + \overline{\psi(z)} = h_1(x, y) + ih_2(x, y), \qquad (3.29)$$

where $K = 1$ for the first boundary value problem, Equation (3.17), and $K = -\kappa$ for the second boundary value problem, Equation (3.18), and where we have introduced a function $\psi(z) \equiv \chi'(z)$.

A very powerful method for solving Equation (3.29) makes use of *conformal mapping* to reduce the problem, for any given region whose boundary L satisfies certain regularity conditions, to a corresponding problem for a region having the unit circle as boundary. Let

$$z = \omega(\zeta) \qquad (3.30)$$

be a function which maps the plane region $z = x + iy$ conformally on the region $\zeta = \xi + i\eta$. Substituting Equation (3.30) into Equation (3.29) and using, for the sake of simplicity, the notation

$$\varphi(z) = \varphi[\omega(\zeta)] \to \varphi(\zeta), \qquad \varphi'(z) = \frac{d\varphi}{d\zeta}\frac{d\zeta}{dz} \to \frac{1}{\omega'(\zeta)}\,\varphi'(\zeta),$$

Equation (3.29), valid on the boundary L of the original region, becomes

$$K\varphi(\sigma) + \frac{\omega(\sigma)}{\omega'(\sigma)}\,\overline{\varphi'(\sigma)} + \overline{\psi(\sigma)} = H(\sigma), \qquad (3.31)$$

valid along the unit circle $\zeta = \sigma$ of the ζ-region, with $|\sigma| = 1$.

Construction of the mapping function $\omega(\zeta)$ constitutes a problem in itself. If $\omega(\zeta)$ can be represented, exactly or with sufficient accuracy, by a polynomial, the solution of Equation (3.31) can be carried out in closed form. For this purpose, a distinction must be made between finite and infinite regions.

(a) Finite, simply connected regions

If the origin $z = 0$ is taken in the interior of the region R, Equation (3.30) can be represented, using power series expansion, as

$$z = \omega(\zeta) = \sum_{k=1}^{\infty}\gamma_k\zeta^k \qquad (3.32)$$

---

† A brief and elementary presentation of the method, with references, may be found in reference [14]. More extensive treatments are contained in references [1] and [2]. The original source is, of course, Muskhelishvili's book, reference [15].

by making the point $z = 0$ correspond to $\zeta = 0$ (Figure 3.2). Since $\bar{\sigma} = 1/\sigma$, we have

$$\overline{\omega'(\sigma)} = \sum_{k=1}^{\infty} k\bar{\gamma}_k \sigma^{-(k-1)}.$$

Terminating the series after a finite number of terms, i.e., replacing it, approximately, by a polynomial,

$$z = \omega(\zeta) = \sum_{k=1}^{n} \gamma_k \zeta^k, \tag{3.33}$$

and expanding $1/\overline{\omega'(\sigma)}$ in a series in powers of $1/\sigma$, we find

$$\frac{\omega(\sigma)}{\overline{\omega'(\sigma)}} = \sum_{k=1}^{n} c_k \sigma^k + R(\sigma), \tag{3.34}$$

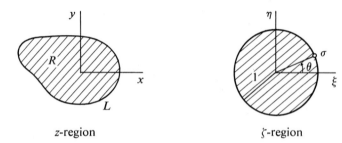

z-region   ζ-region

Figure 3.2

where

$$R(\sigma) = \sum_{k=0}^{\infty} \frac{c_{-k}}{\sigma^k}.$$

$R(\sigma)$ will not be needed in the following.

The function $H(\sigma)$ in Equation (3.31) is obtained as the (complex) Fourier expansion of the given function $h_1 + ih_2$ on the unit circle $\zeta = \sigma = e^{i\theta} = \cos\theta + i\sin\theta$, where θ is the polar angle (Figure 3.2). Thus,

$$\left.\begin{array}{l} H(\sigma) = h_1(x, y) + ih_2(x, y) = \sum_{k=-\infty}^{+\infty} A_k \sigma^k, \\[2mm] A_k = \frac{1}{2\pi} \int_0^{2\pi} (h_1 + ih_2)e^{-ik\theta}\, d\theta. \end{array}\right\} \tag{3.35}$$

In order to determine the unknown functions $\varphi(\zeta)$ and $\psi(\zeta)$ representing the solution of the problem, we make use of the fact that these functions will be holomorphic in the interior $|\zeta| < 1$ and on the boundary $|\zeta| = 1$ of the unit circle, provided there are no singularities, i.e., no single forces or point sources of heat present in the region R or on the boundary L. Hence, we may write

$$\varphi(\zeta) = \sum_{k=0}^{\infty} a_k \zeta^k, \qquad \psi(\zeta) = \sum_{k=0}^{\infty} b_k \zeta^k. \qquad (3.36)$$

Using Equation (3.34), we then have

$$\frac{\omega(\sigma)}{\omega'(\sigma)} \overline{\varphi'(\sigma)} = \left[\sum_{k=1}^{n} c_k \sigma^k + R(\sigma) \right] \sum_{k=1}^{\infty} \frac{k \bar{a}_k}{\sigma^{k-1}} = \sum_{k=0}^{n} B_k \sigma^k + \sum_{k=1}^{\infty} \frac{B_{-k}}{\sigma^k}, \quad (3.37)$$

where

$$\left. \begin{array}{l} B_n = \bar{a}_1 c_n, \\[4pt] B_{n-1} = \bar{a}_1 c_{n-1} + 2\bar{a}_2 c_n, \\[4pt] \qquad \cdot \\[2pt] \qquad \cdot \\[2pt] \qquad \cdot \\[4pt] B_2 = \bar{a}_1 c_2 + 2\bar{a}_2 c_3 + \ldots + (n-1)\bar{a}_{n-1} c_n, \\[4pt] B_1 = \bar{a}_1 c_1 + 2\bar{a}_2 c_2 + \ldots + n\bar{a}_n c_n. \end{array} \right\} \qquad (3.38)$$

Coefficients B_0, B_{-1}, ... , will not be needed.

Substituting, now, Equations (3.35), (3.36), and (3.37) into Equation (3.31), we obtain

$$K \sum_{k=0}^{\infty} a_k \sigma^k + \sum_{k=0}^{n} B_k \sigma^k + \sum_{k=1}^{\infty} \frac{B_{-k}}{\sigma^k} + \sum_{k=0}^{\infty} \frac{\bar{b}_k}{\sigma^k} = \sum_{k=-\infty}^{+\infty} A_k \sigma^k. \qquad (3.39)$$

Comparison of coefficients of equal nonnegative powers of σ yields a set of equations for the a_k

$$\left. \begin{array}{l} Ka_0 + B_0 + \bar{b}_0 = A_0, \\[4pt] Ka_k + B_k = A_k \qquad (k = 1, 2, \ldots, n), \\[4pt] Ka_k = A_k, \qquad k > n. \end{array} \right\} \qquad (3.40)$$

We note from the first of these equations that without loss of generality, we may put $a_0 = 0$. This is also obvious from Equations (3.10) and (3.12). Comparison of coefficients of negative powers in Equation (3.39) would give the coefficients b_k. It is, however, more convenient to take the conjugate complex of Equation (3.31):

$$\psi(\sigma) = \overline{H(\sigma)} - \frac{\overline{\omega(\sigma)}}{\overline{\omega'(\sigma)}} \, \varphi'(\sigma) - K\overline{\varphi(\sigma)}.$$

From the preceding, with $a_0 = 0$,

$$K\varphi(\sigma) = \sum_{k=1}^{\infty} A_k \sigma^k - \sum_{k=1}^{n} B_k \sigma^k.$$

Hence, using Equation (3.35),

$$\psi(\sigma) = \sum_{k=-\infty}^{0} \bar{A}_k \sigma^{-k} - \overline{\frac{\omega(\sigma)}{\omega'(\sigma)}}\, \varphi'(\sigma) + \sum_{k=1}^{n} \bar{B}_k \sigma^{-k},$$

whence follows, by replacing σ by ζ and $\bar{\sigma}$ by $1/\zeta$,

$$\psi(\zeta) = \sum_{k=-\infty}^{0} \bar{A}_k \zeta^{-k} - \frac{\bar{\omega}(1/\zeta)}{\omega'(\zeta)}\, \varphi'(\zeta) + \sum_{k=1}^{n} \bar{B}_k \zeta^{-k}. \tag{3.41}$$

This also determines $b_0 = \psi(0)$ and, hence, B_0 from the first of Equations (3.40).

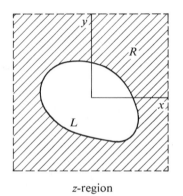
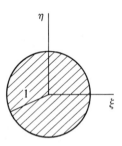

z-region ζ-region

Figure 3.3

(b) Infinite region

Let the infinite region R be the exterior of a closed curve L, and let the origin $z = 0$ of the coordinate system be taken in the interior of this curve (Figure 3.3). Then, by making the point $z = \infty$ correspond to the origin $\zeta = 0$ in the image plane, the function

$$z = \omega(\zeta) = \frac{c}{\zeta} + \sum_{k=0}^{\infty} \gamma_k \zeta^k \tag{3.42}$$

maps the region R with boundary L onto the unit circle $|\zeta| \leqslant 1$. No higher negative powers can be present in $\omega(\zeta)$ if it is to represent a one-to-one mapping.

We now have

$$\overline{\omega'(\sigma)} = -c\sigma^2 + \sum_{k=1}^{n} k\bar{\gamma}_k \sigma^{-(k-1)}$$

if, as before, we replace the infinite series in Equation (3.42) by a polynomial.

Then,

$$\frac{\omega(\sigma)}{\omega'(\sigma)} = \sum_{k=1}^{n-2} c_k \sigma^k + R(\sigma), \tag{3.43}$$

where $R(\sigma)$ has the same form as in Equation (3.34).

We turn now to the structure of the functions $\varphi(\zeta)$ and $\psi(\zeta)$. It can be shown† that in the most general case where nonequilibrating external stresses with resultants S_x and S_y act along the hole, and where the stresses at infinity do not vanish, $\varphi(\zeta)$ and $\psi(\zeta)$ will have the form

$$\left.\begin{aligned} \varphi(\zeta) &= \frac{S_x + iS_y}{2\pi(1 + \kappa)} \log \zeta + \beta \frac{c}{\zeta} + \sum_{k=1}^{\infty} a_k \zeta^k, \\[2mm] \psi(\zeta) &= -\kappa \frac{S_x - iS_y}{2\pi(1 + \kappa)} \log \zeta + (\beta' + i\gamma')\frac{c}{\zeta} + \sum_{k=0}^{\infty} b_k \zeta^k. \end{aligned}\right\} \tag{3.44}$$

It follows from Equations (3.10), using Equation (3.42) and letting $\zeta \to 0$, that the real constants β, β', and γ' are related to the stresses at infinity by

$$\left.\begin{aligned} \sigma_{xx} + \sigma_{yy} + 4G\lambda\Theta\big|_{\infty} &= 8G\beta, \\[2mm] \sigma_{yy} - \sigma_{xx} + 2G\left(\frac{\partial^2\Phi}{\partial x^2} - \frac{\partial^2\Phi}{\partial y^2}\right)\bigg|_{\infty} &= 8G\beta', \\[2mm] \sigma_{xy} - 4G\frac{\partial^2\Phi}{\partial x\partial y}\bigg|_{\infty} &= 4G\gamma', \end{aligned}\right\} \tag{3.45}$$

λ is to be taken from either Equation (3.11) or (3.23) for plane strain or plane stress, respectively. In problems of thermoelasticity, we shall, in general, have $S_x = S_y = 0$.

Proceeding in the same manner as in Case (a), we have first, in place of Equations (3.37) and (3.38):

$$\frac{\omega(\sigma)}{\omega'(\sigma)} \overline{\varphi'(\sigma)} = \sum_{k=0}^{n-2} B_k \sigma^k + \sum_{k=1}^{\infty} \frac{B_{-k}}{\sigma^k}, \tag{3.46}$$

where

$$\left.\begin{aligned} B_{n-2} &= \bar{a}_1 c_{n-2}, \\ B_{n-3} &= \bar{a}_1 c_{n-3} + 2\bar{a}_2 c_{n-2}, \\ &\ \ \vdots \\ &\ \ \vdots \\ B_1 &= \bar{a}_1 c_1 + 2\bar{a}_2 c_2 + \cdots + (n-2)\bar{a}_{n-2} c_{n-2}. \end{aligned}\right\} \tag{3.47}$$

---

† See, for instance, reference [1], p. 279.

The other equations in Case (*a*) remain unchanged except for *n* which has to be replaced by $n - 2$.

3.5. Curvilinear Coordinates

Let the *z*-plane and the ζ-plane (Figure 3.4), be connected by the mapping function $z = \omega(\zeta)$. Since conformal mapping preserves angles, the lines

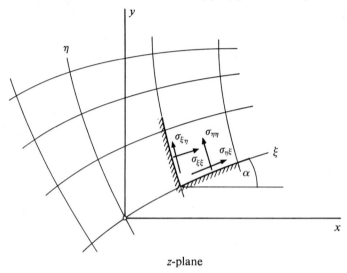

z-plane

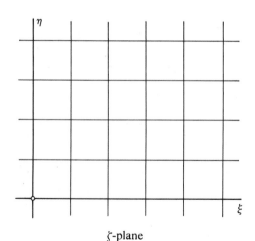

ζ-plane

Figure 3.4

ξ = const. and η = const. form, in the z-plane, an orthogonal curvilinear network. It is shown in complex function theory that the angle α between the ξ-lines and the x-axis is given by

$$e^{2i\alpha} = \frac{\omega'(\zeta)}{\overline{\omega'(\zeta)}}.$$ (3.48)

In order to find the stress components $\sigma_{\xi\xi}$, $\sigma_{\eta\eta}$, $\sigma_{\xi\eta}$ in the curvilinear coordinate system ξ, η, we use the well-known relations

$$\left.\begin{aligned}
2\sigma_{\xi\xi} &= \sigma_{xx} + \sigma_{yy} + (\sigma_{xx} - \sigma_{yy})\cos 2\alpha + 2\sigma_{xy}\sin 2\alpha, \\
2\sigma_{\xi\eta} &= -(\sigma_{xx} - \sigma_{yy})\sin 2\alpha + 2\sigma_{xy}\cos 2\alpha.
\end{aligned}\right\}$$ (3.49)

In complex form, this may be written as

$$2(\sigma_{\xi\xi} + i\sigma_{\xi\eta}) = \sigma_{xx} + \sigma_{yy} + (\sigma_{xx} - \sigma_{yy} + 2i\sigma_{xy})e^{-2i\alpha}.$$

Utilizing, in addition, the fact that the sum of the normal stresses is an invariant under rotation of the coordinate system, we obtain

$$\left.\begin{aligned}
\sigma_{\xi\xi} + \sigma_{\eta\eta} &= \sigma_{xx} + \sigma_{yy}, \\
\sigma_{\xi\xi} - \sigma_{\eta\eta} + 2i\sigma_{\xi\eta} &= (\sigma_{xx} - \sigma_{yy} + 2i\sigma_{xy})e^{-2i\alpha}.
\end{aligned}\right\}$$ (3.50)

As a special case, we introduce polar coordinates $z = re^{i\theta}$ and consider the mapping

$$\omega(\zeta) = e^{\zeta} \qquad \text{or} \qquad re^{i\theta} = e^{\xi + i\eta},$$

whence $e^{\xi} = r$, $\eta = \theta$. The lines ξ = const. are, therefore, the circles r = const. and the lines η = const. are the radial lines θ = const. Hence, the stress components in polar coordinates are,

$$\left.\begin{aligned}
\sigma_{rr} + \sigma_{\theta\theta} &= \sigma_{xx} + \sigma_{yy}, \\
\sigma_{rr} - \sigma_{\theta\theta} + 2i\sigma_{r\theta} &= (\sigma_{xx} - \sigma_{yy} + 2i\sigma_{xy})\bar{z}/z.
\end{aligned}\right\}$$ (3.51)

The equations of equilibrium in polar coordinates read

$$\left.\begin{aligned}
\frac{\partial \sigma_{rr}}{\partial r} + \frac{1}{r}\frac{\partial \sigma_{\theta r}}{\partial \theta} + \frac{\sigma_{rr} - \sigma_{\theta\theta}}{r} &= 0, \\
\frac{\partial \sigma_{r\theta}}{\partial r} + \frac{1}{r}\frac{\partial \sigma_{\theta\theta}}{\partial \theta} + \frac{2}{r}\sigma_{r\theta} &= 0,
\end{aligned}\right\}$$ (3.52)

and will be satisfied identically by setting

$$\left.\begin{aligned}
\sigma_{rr} &= \frac{1}{r}\frac{\partial F}{\partial r} + \frac{1}{r^2}\frac{\partial^2 F}{\partial \theta^2}, \qquad \sigma_{\theta\theta} = \frac{\partial^2 F}{\partial r^2}, \\
\sigma_{r\theta} &= \sigma_{\theta r} = \frac{1}{r^2}\frac{\partial F}{\partial \theta} - \frac{1}{r}\frac{\partial^2 F}{\partial r\partial\theta} \equiv -\frac{\partial}{\partial r}\left(\frac{1}{r}\frac{\partial F}{\partial \theta}\right),
\end{aligned}\right\} \tag{3.53}$$

where $F(r, \theta)$ is Airy's stress function, Equation (3.8). Using these equations together with Equations (3.51) and (3.10), we obtain the following relations

$$\left.\begin{aligned}
\sigma_{rr} + \sigma_{\theta\theta} &= 4G[\varphi'(z) + \overline{\varphi'(z)} - \lambda\Theta], \\
\sigma_{rr} - \sigma_{\theta\theta} + 2i\sigma_{r\theta} &= 2G\left[2\frac{\partial^2 \Phi}{\partial r^2} - \nabla^2\Phi + 2i\frac{\partial}{\partial r}\left(\frac{1}{r}\frac{\partial \Phi}{\partial \theta}\right)\right] \\
&\quad - 4G\left[\bar{z}\overline{\varphi''(z)} + \frac{\bar{z}}{z}\overline{\psi'(z)}\right].
\end{aligned}\right\} \tag{3.54}$$

Here,

$$\nabla^2\Phi = \frac{\partial^2 \Phi}{\partial r^2} + \frac{1}{r}\frac{\partial \Phi}{\partial r} + \frac{1}{r^2}\frac{\partial^2 \Phi}{\partial \theta^2}, \tag{3.55}$$

and Φ is again given by either Equation (3.5) or (3.22) for the case of plane strain or plane stress, respectively.

3.6. Two-Dimensional Stress-Free Temperature Fields

In Section 2.3, necessary and sufficient conditions were obtained for the temperature field for the body to remain free of stress. Of course, these conditions are also valid for two-dimensional fields. If, however, for a cylinder in a state of plane strain, the requirement of a totally stress-free body is relaxed so that only the stresses σ_{xx}, σ_{xy}, σ_{zz} are required to vanish while axial stresses σ_{zz} are admitted, Equation (2.23) may be replaced by a less stringent condition.

We restrict out attention to stationary temperature fields $\Theta(x, y)$ with no heat sources present within the body. Equation (2.16) then holds:

$$\frac{\partial^2 \Theta}{\partial x^2} + \frac{\partial^2 \Theta}{\partial y^2} = 0. \tag{3.56}$$

The plane harmonic function Θ may be combined with its conjugate harmonic function $\rho(x, y)$ into the analytic function

$$p(z) = \Theta(x, y) + i\rho(x, y). \tag{3.57}$$

If the stresses σ_{xx}, σ_{xy}, and σ_{yy} are to vanish, it follows from Equations (3.3) that

$$\varepsilon_{xx} = \varepsilon_{yy} = (1 + \nu)\alpha\Theta, \qquad \varepsilon_{xy} = 0.$$

Hence, the displacements $u(x, y)$ and $v(x, y)$ satisfy the Cauchy-Riemann equations,

$$\frac{\partial u}{\partial x} = \frac{\partial v}{\partial y}, \qquad \frac{\partial u}{\partial y} = -\frac{\partial v}{\partial x},$$

and the function

$$P(z) = u(x, y) + iv(x, y) \tag{3.58}$$

is analytic. Differentiating and using the preceding equations, we obtain

$$P'(z) = (1 + \nu)\alpha p(z),$$

and hence

$$P(z) = (1 + \nu)\alpha \int p(z)\, dz. \tag{3.59}$$

Now, if the displacement field corresponding to the stress-free temperature field is to be kinematically possible, u and v must be single-valued functions. Hence, $P(z)$ must be single-valued. Thus, if $P(a)$ and $P(b)$ are the values of P at the two points $z = a$ and $z = b$, the difference $P(b) - P(a)$ must vanish if a and b coincide. It therefore follows from Equation (3.59) that

$$\oint_C p(z)\, dz = 0 \tag{3.60}$$

along any closed curve C lying entirely within the cross section of the cylinder.

Equation (3.60) replaces Equation (2.23). Together with Equation (3.56), it constitutes a necessary and sufficient condition for the temperature field to be stress-free.

If the cross section R is simply connected, Equation (3.60) will be automatically satisfied if Equation (3.56) is satisfied everywhere in the region R, since there will then be no singularities of Θ, and hence of P, within any closed curve in this region. If, however, the cross section is multiply connected, containing one or more holes, the condition of Equation (3.60) will be violated whenever there is a singularity outside of the body, but within one of the holes. The following examples illustrate this fact for a body with one hole (Figure 3.5).

Example (a)

Let $p(z) = K \log z$. Putting $z = re^{i\theta}$, we obtain $\Theta = K \log r$. This corresponds to a line source of heat located along $z = 0$. Equation (3.56) is satisfied within the shaded region R, but Equation (3.60) is violated for any closed curve C enclosing the hole:

$$\oint_C p(z)\, dz = 2\pi i K z \neq 0.$$

The body will not remain free of stress.

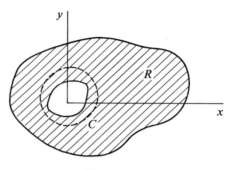

Figure 3.5

Example (b)

Let $p(z) = K/z$. The temperature distribution $\Theta = K/r \cos \theta$ corresponds to a doublet (dipole) at $z = 0$. Again, Equation (3.60) is not satisfied:

$$\oint_C p(z) \, dz = 2\pi i K \neq 0.$$

The temperature field will produce stress.

3.7. Example: Plate with Circular Hole in Uniform Heat Flow

In an infinite plate (Figure 3.6), heat is flowing uniformly in the direction of the negative y-axis, $\Theta = qy$, where q is the constant temperature gradient.

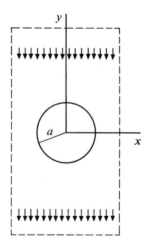

Figure 3.6

No stress is produced by this linear temperature field. The uniform flow of heat is disturbed by the presence of an insulated circular hole of radius a. Localized thermal stresses will then appear.†

The solution of the heat equation $\nabla^2\Theta = 0$, satisfying the boundary condition $\partial\Theta/\partial r = 0$ at $r = a$, is given by

$$\Theta = q\left(y + \frac{a^2}{r}\sin\theta\right). \tag{3.61}$$

In determining the thermoelastic potential from Equation (3.22) the uniform heat flow may be disregarded. Then,

$$\nabla^2\Phi = \frac{\partial^2\Phi}{\partial r^2} + \frac{1}{r}\frac{\partial\Phi}{\partial r} + \frac{1}{r^2}\frac{\partial^2\Phi}{\partial\theta^2} = (1 + \nu)\alpha q\,\frac{a^2}{r}\sin\theta.$$

A particular solution is

$$\Phi = \frac{(1 + \nu)\alpha q}{2}\,a^2 r\log r\sin\theta. \tag{3.62}$$

We employ the complex function approach. The function

$$z = \omega(\zeta) = \frac{a}{\zeta} \tag{3.63}$$

maps the exterior of the circle $|z| = a$ in the z-plane onto the interior of the unit circle $|\zeta| = 1$ in the ζ-plane (Figure 3.3). Then $\overline{\omega'(\sigma)} = -a\sigma^2$, and

$$\frac{\overline{\omega(\sigma)}}{\omega'(\sigma)} = -\frac{1}{\sigma^3}.$$

No external stresses act at the boundary of the hole. Thus, the function $H(\sigma)$ in Equation (3.31) is, from Equation (3.17),

$$H(\sigma) = \left(\frac{\partial\Phi}{\partial x} + i\frac{\partial\Phi}{\partial y}\right)_{r=a} + C = \frac{(1 + \nu)\alpha q}{2}\,[xy + iy^2 + ia^2\log a] + C$$

$$= \frac{(1 + \nu)\alpha q}{4}\,iz(\bar{z} - z)\bigg|_{|z|=a} = \frac{(1 + \nu)\alpha q}{4}\,ia^2\left(1 - \frac{1}{\sigma^2}\right).$$

The constant C has been chosen to cancel the constant term in $H(\sigma)$. Stresses and temperature vanish at infinity. Hence, according to Equations (3.44) and (3.45),

$$\varphi(\zeta) = \sum_{k=1}^{\infty} a_k\zeta^k, \qquad \psi(\zeta) = \sum_{k=0}^{\infty} b_k\zeta^k. \tag{3.64}$$

---

† See reference [16].

Substituting into Equation (3.31) with $K = 1$, we get

$$\sum_{k=1}^{\infty}\left(a_k \sigma^k - \frac{k\bar{a}_k}{\sigma^{k+2}}\right) + \sum_{k=0}^{\infty}\frac{\bar{b}_k}{\sigma^k} = \frac{(1+\nu)\alpha q}{4} ia^2\left(1 - \frac{1}{\sigma^2}\right).$$

Comparison of coefficients renders $\bar{b}_0 = (1+\nu)\alpha qia^2/4$, $\bar{b}_2 = -\bar{b}_0$. All other coefficients are zero. Therefore, the solution is

$$\varphi(\zeta) = 0, \qquad \psi(\zeta) = -\frac{(1+\nu)\alpha q}{4}ia^2(1-\zeta^2).$$

In the z-plane:

$$\varphi(z) = 0, \qquad \psi(z) = -\frac{(1+\nu)\alpha q}{4}ia^2\left(1 - \frac{a^2}{z^2}\right).$$

The stresses follow from Equation (3.54), using the first of Equations (3.23) and $E = 2(1+\nu)G$, as

$$\sigma_{rr} + \sigma_{\theta\theta} = -E\alpha\Theta = -E\alpha q\frac{a^2}{r}\sin\theta,$$

$$\sigma_{rr} - \sigma_{\theta\theta} + 2i\sigma_{r\theta} = E\alpha qa\left[\frac{a^3}{r^3}\sin\theta + i\left(\frac{a}{r} - \frac{a^3}{r^3}\right)\cos\theta\right],$$

or, after separation,

$$\left.\begin{array}{c}\sigma_{rr} = -\dfrac{E\alpha qa}{2}\left(\dfrac{a}{r} - \dfrac{a^3}{r^3}\right)\sin\theta, \qquad \sigma_{\theta\theta} = -\dfrac{E\alpha qa}{2}\left(\dfrac{a}{r} + \dfrac{a^3}{r^3}\right)\sin\theta, \\[3mm] \sigma_{r\theta} = \dfrac{E\alpha qa}{2}\left(\dfrac{a}{r} - \dfrac{a^3}{r^3}\right)\cos\theta.\end{array}\right\} \quad (3.65)$$

The maximum stress $E\alpha qa$ is obtained on the boundary $r = a$ at the two poles $\theta = \pi/2$ and $\theta = 3\pi/2$. It is compressive at the hot pole and tensile at the cool pole.

3.8. Example: Point Source in a Semi-Infinite Plate

At the point $(\xi, 0)$ of a semi-infinite plate $x \geqslant 0$, a heat source is located (Figure 3.7). The surface $x = 0$ is free of applied stress and is kept at temperature $\Theta = 0$.

The temperature field produced by the heat source in an infinite plate is $\Theta = -K\log r_1$, with $M = 2\pi khK$ as the strength of the source. The thickness of the plate is h, the thermal conductivity is k. To satisfy the boundary condition $\Theta = 0$ on $x = 0$, we extend the disk to cover the entire x, y-plane and place a sink of equal strength at the point $(-\xi, 0)$. The temperature field is then

$$\Theta = K\log\frac{r_2}{r_1}. \tag{3.66}$$

Equation (3.22) furnishes the thermoelastic potential

$$\Phi = \frac{(1 + \nu)\alpha K}{4} \left[r_2^2(\log r_2 - 1) - r_1^2(\log r_1 - 1) \right].$$

We use the real function approach and take Ψ in Equation (3.24) in the form of a Fourier integral, symmetric with respect to y. Utilizing Equations (3.26), we put

$$\Psi(x, y) = \frac{(1 + \nu)\alpha K}{4} \int_0^\infty \frac{1}{\mu^2} (A + \mu x B) e^{-\mu x} \cos \mu y \, d\mu, \qquad (3.67)$$

where A and B are as yet undetermined functions of μ. From Equations (3.2)

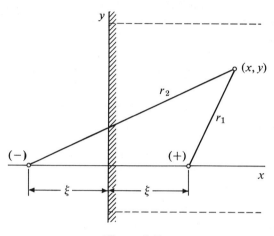

Figure 3.7

with $F = 2G(\Psi - \Phi)$, we have, writing $2G(1 + \nu)\alpha K/4 = E\alpha K/4 = C$,

$$\sigma_{xx} = C\left\{ -\int_0^\infty (A + \mu x B) e^{-\mu x} \cos \mu y \, d\mu - 2\left[\log \frac{r_2}{r_1} + y^2\left(\frac{1}{r_2^2} - \frac{1}{r_1^2} \right) \right] \right\},$$

$$\sigma_{xy} = C\left\{ -\int_0^\infty (A - B + \mu x B) e^{-\mu x} \sin \mu y \, d\mu + 2\left(\frac{x + \xi}{r_2^2} - \frac{x - \xi}{r_1^2} \right) y \right\}.$$

$$(3.68)$$

Boundary conditions require $\sigma_{xx} = \sigma_{xy} = 0$ at $x = 0$, while all stresses are to vanish at infinity. This furnishes two equations for A and B:

$$\int_0^\infty A \cos \mu y \, d\mu = 0, \qquad \int_0^\infty (A - B) \sin \mu y \, d\mu = \frac{4\xi y}{\xi^2 + y^2}.$$

From the first, we have $A = 0$. Expanding $y/(\xi^2 + y^2)$ in the second equation in a Fourier integral,

$$\frac{y}{\xi^2 + y^2} = \int_0^\infty e^{-\mu\xi} \sin \mu y \, d\mu$$

and substituting, we obtain $B = -4\xi e^{-\mu\xi}$. However, the integral in Equation (3.67) becomes divergent upon substitution of A and B. Nevertheless, by proceeding formally, Ψ may be determined in closed form by first evaluating the convergent integral representation for $\partial\Psi/\partial y$ and then integrating the result with respect to y. We obtain,

$$2G\Psi = 4C\xi x \log r_2.$$

This function may easily be shown to satisfy the biharmonic equation (3.25) while the corresponding stresses satisfy all boundary conditions. Thus, the final result is

$$
\left.
\begin{aligned}
\sigma_{xx} &= 2C\left[2\xi x \frac{(x+\xi)^2 - y^2}{r_2^4} - \log \frac{r_2}{r_1} + y^2\left(\frac{1}{r_1^2} - \frac{1}{r_2^2}\right) \right], \\
\sigma_{yy} &= 2C\left[2\xi \frac{r_2^2(x+2\xi) + 2xy^2}{r_2^4} - \log \frac{r_2}{r_1} + \frac{(x-\xi)^2}{r_1^2} - \frac{(x+\xi)^2}{r_2^2} \right], \\
\sigma_{xy} &= 2C\left[2\xi y \frac{x^2 - y^2 - a^2}{r_2^4} + y\left(\frac{x+\xi}{r_2^2} - \frac{x-\xi}{r_1^2}\right) \right].
\end{aligned}
\right\} \quad (3.69)
$$

- *Problems*

1. Derive Equation (3.28).

   HINT: Let unit radial stresses f act uniformly at the surface of a cylinder of radius ρ. Follow the argument on p. 19.

2. Compute the axial stress σ_{zz} corresponding to a two-dimensional temperature field which is stress-free in the sense of Section 3.6.

   HINT: Use Equation (3.14).

3. Determine the displacements in Example (a) of Section 3.6 and show that they would have to be discontinuous if the cylinder is to be free of stress.

   HINT: Use Equation (3.59) for $P(z)$ and separate into real and imaginary parts to obtain

   $$u = (1 + \nu)\alpha K[x(\log r - 1) - y\theta], \qquad v = (1 + \nu)\alpha K[y(\log r - 1) + x\theta].$$

   Going once around the hole, θ is increased by 2π. Hence, u and v experience a jump of magnitude $-2\pi(1 + \nu)\alpha Ky$ and $2\pi(1 + \nu)\alpha Kx$, respectively. Such a discontinuity is possible only if the cylinder is cut along some radial line making it simply connected (and free of stress!).

4. Determine the displacements corresponding to Example (b) of Section 3.6 and show that v is discontinuous.

HINT: Proceed as in Problem 3 above.

5. Solve the problem of Section 3.7 using the real function approach.

HINT: Use Equations (3.53) to express the boundary conditions $\sigma_{rr} = \sigma_{r\theta} = 0$ in terms of $F = 2G(\Psi - \Phi)$, where Φ is given by Equation (3.62). Select Ψ from the set of Equations (3.27).

ATTENTION: Since $\nabla^2\Theta = 0$ here, Φ is itself a biharmonic function. Do not eliminate it unintentionally from the solution by including it in the set Ψ.

6. Heat is flowing uniformly in the radial direction from the inner surface $r = a$ of a long circular tube to the outer surface $r = b$ which is at zero temperature. Both surfaces are free of applied stress. Determine the stress in the tube using the real function method.

HINT: The temperature distribution corresponds to a line source located on the axis of the tube and is given by† $\Theta = K \log b/r$. A particular solution of Equation (3.5) will have the form $\Phi = C_1 r^2 + C_2 r^2 \log b/r$. Determine C_1 and C_2. Let Ψ in Equation (3.24) be $\Psi = Ar^2 + B \log r$ [see Equations (3.27)], and use Equations (3.53) together with the boundary conditions to determine A and B. The result is

$$\sigma_{rr} = \frac{-E\alpha}{2(1-v)}\left[\Theta(r) - \frac{a^2 b^2 - r^2}{r^2 b^2 - a^2}\Theta(a)\right],$$

$$\sigma_{r\theta} = 0,$$

$$\sigma_{\theta\theta} = \frac{-E\alpha}{2(1-v)}\left[\Theta(r) + \frac{a^2 b^2 + r^2}{r^2 b^2 - a^2}\Theta(a) - K\right].$$

7. An infinite plate contains a rigid circular inclusion of radius a. The plate is heated to a uniform temperature Θ. Determine the stress using the complex method.

HINT: Putting $(1 + v)\alpha\Theta = C$, the thermoelastic potential is $\Phi = Cr^2/4$ from Equation (3.22). To satisfy the boundary condition $u = v = 0$ at $r = a$ apply the mapping (3.63) and determine $H(\sigma) = Ca/2\sigma$. From Equations (3.44) and (3.45) note that $\varphi(\zeta) = \beta a/\zeta + \sum_1^\infty a_k\zeta^k$ and $\psi(\zeta) = \sum_0^\infty b_k\zeta^k$. Substitute into Equation (3.31) with $K = -\kappa$ and compare coefficients. It follows that

$$\varphi = \frac{Ca}{4\zeta} = \frac{Cz}{4}, \qquad \psi = \frac{(1 + \kappa)Ca\zeta}{4} = \frac{(1 + \kappa)Ca^2}{4z}.$$

Equations (3.54) then give

$$\sigma_{rr} = -\sigma_{\theta\theta} = \frac{1 + \kappa}{2}\frac{GCa^2}{r^2} = \frac{2G\alpha\Theta_0 a^2}{r^2}, \qquad \sigma_{r\theta} = 0.$$

8. Solve Problem 7 using the real function method.

HINT: Write the boundary condition at $r = a$ in the form $\varepsilon_{\theta\theta} = 0$ and let $\Psi = Ar^2 + B \log r$.

---

† See Equation (2.18).

CHAPTER 4

Thermal Bending and Buckling of Plates

THE THEORY OF plates at uniform temperature and loaded perpendicular to the midplane is well developed, and an extensive literature exists on the subject. In this chapter we shall extend this theory to include non-uniform temperature.

4.1. Bending and Stretching

Let a thin plate (Figure 4.1), be exposed to an arbitrary temperature distribution $\Theta(x, y, z)$. The stresses produced by the variation of Θ with respect to x, y have already been considered in Section 3.2 and will be termed "membrane stresses." The stresses caused by the variation of Θ across the thickness of the plate are "bending stresses." The plate will, in general, not only stretch in its midplane, but also deflect under the action of Θ.

In deriving the basic equations the following simplifying assumptions will be made. They are extensions to two dimensions of the assumptions used in the theory of bending of beams.

(1) The normal to the midplane of the plate remains normal to the deflected midsurface with negligible change in length,† that is, $\varepsilon_{xz} = \varepsilon_{yz} = \varepsilon_{zz} = 0$.

(2) Normal stresses in the direction of the plate thickness are neglected, that is, $\sigma_{zz} = 0$. Hooke's law then takes on the form of Equations (3.19).

(3) Membrane (midplane) stresses arising from the deflection of the plate are neglected. This assumption restricts the theory to small deflections. Equations (2.10) may, therefore, be used.

---

† This assumption is termed Kirchhoff's hypothesis and is the equivalent to Bernoulli's hypothesis in beam theory.

From assumption (1), using Equations (2.10a), it follows

$$\varepsilon_{zz} = \frac{\partial w}{\partial z} = 0, \qquad \varepsilon_{xz} = \frac{\partial u}{\partial z} + \frac{\partial w}{\partial x} = 0, \qquad \varepsilon_{yz} = \frac{\partial v}{\partial z} + \frac{\partial w}{\partial y} = 0.$$

Therefore, the deflection w does not depend on the distance z from the midplane. If the displacements of points in the midplane are denoted by u_0, v_0, and w_0, and the corresponding strain components by ε_{xx}^0, ε_{yy}^0, and ε_{xy}^0, we have

$$w(x, y, z) = w_0(x, y), \qquad (4.1)$$

and

$$u(x, y, z) = u_0(x, y) - z \frac{\partial w}{\partial x}, \qquad v(x, y, z) = v_0(x, y) - z \frac{\partial w}{\partial y}. \quad (4.2)$$

Hence, taking account of Equations (3.19), we obtain the strain components

$$\left. \begin{aligned} \varepsilon_{xx} &= \varepsilon_{xx}^0 - z \frac{\partial^2 w}{\partial x^2} = \frac{1}{E} (\sigma_{xx} - \nu\sigma_{yy}) + \alpha\Theta, \\ \varepsilon_{yy} &= \varepsilon_{yy}^0 - z \frac{\partial^2 w}{\partial y^2} = \frac{1}{E} (\sigma_{yy} - \nu\sigma_{xx}) + \alpha\Theta, \\ \varepsilon_{xy} &= \varepsilon_{xy}^0 - 2z \frac{\partial^2 w}{\partial x \, \partial y} = \frac{2(1 + \nu)}{E} \sigma_{xy}. \end{aligned} \right\} \qquad (4.3)$$

It is convenient in plate theory to operate with stress resultants per unit length of a line in the midplane rather than with stresses. We define membrane forces n_x, n_y, n_{xy}, bending moments m_x, m_y, and twisting moments m_{xy} acting on an element of the plate as shown in Figure 4.1:

$$n_x = \int_{-h/2}^{+h/2} \sigma_{xx} \, dz, \qquad n_y = \int_{-h/2}^{+h/2} \sigma_{yy} \, dz, \qquad n_{xy} = n_{yx} = \int_{-h/2}^{+h/2} \sigma_{xy} \, dz,$$

$$m_x = \int_{-h/2}^{+h/2} \sigma_{xx} z \, dz, \qquad m_y = \int_{-h/2}^{+h/2} \sigma_{yy} z \, dz, \qquad m_{xy} = m_{yx} = \int_{-h/2}^{+h/2} \sigma_{xy} z \, dz.$$

$$(4.4)$$

Solving Equations (4.3) for the stresses and substituting into Equations (4.4), we obtain

$$\left. \begin{aligned} n_x &= D[\varepsilon_{xx}^0 + \nu\varepsilon_{yy}^0 - (1 + \nu)\alpha n_\Theta], \\ n_y &= D[\varepsilon_{yy}^0 + \nu\varepsilon_{xx}^0 - (1 + \nu)\alpha n_\Theta], \\ n_{xy} &= n_{yx} = \frac{1 - \nu}{2} D\varepsilon_{xy}^0, \end{aligned} \right\} \qquad (4.5)$$

$$m_x = -K\left[\frac{\partial^2 w}{\partial x^2} + \nu \frac{\partial^2 w}{\partial y^2} + (1 + \nu)\alpha m_\Theta\right],$$

$$m_y = -K\left[\frac{\partial^2 w}{\partial y^2} + \nu \frac{\partial^2 w}{\partial x^2} + (1 + \nu)\alpha m_\Theta\right],$$

$$m_{xy} = m_{yx} = -(1 - \nu)K\frac{\partial^2 w}{\partial x \partial y}.$$

$$(4.6)$$

The two constants

$$D = \frac{Eh}{1 - \nu^2}, \qquad K = \frac{Eh^3}{12(1 - \nu^2)} \qquad (4.7)$$

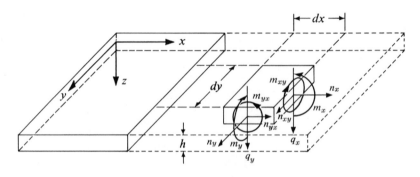

Figure 4.1

are stretching stiffness and bending stiffness, respectively, while

$$n_\Theta = \frac{1}{h}\int_{-h/2}^{+h/2} \Theta \, dz, \qquad m_\Theta = \frac{12}{h^3}\int_{-h/2}^{+h/2} \Theta z \, dz \qquad (4.8)$$

represent mean temperature and temperature moment, respectively.

Once the stress resultants are known, the stresses may be computed from the following equations:

$$\sigma_{xx} = \frac{n_x}{h} + \frac{12m_x}{h^3}z + \frac{E\alpha}{1 - \nu}(n_\Theta - \Theta + zm_\Theta),$$

$$\sigma_{yy} = \frac{n_y}{h} + \frac{12m_y}{h^3}z + \frac{E\alpha}{1 - \nu}(n_\Theta - \Theta + zm_\Theta),$$

$$\sigma_{xy} = \frac{n_{xy}}{h} + \frac{12m_{xy}}{h^3}z.$$

$$(4.9)$$

4.2. Equilibrium

We consider an element of the plate (Figure 4.1). Equilibrium in the directions of x and y yields the two conditions

$$\frac{\partial n_x}{\partial x} + \frac{\partial n_{yx}}{\partial y} = 0, \qquad \frac{\partial n_{xy}}{\partial x} + \frac{\partial n_y}{\partial y} = 0 \qquad (4.10)$$

in agreement with Equations (3.1). In addition, Equations (4.5) are identical with Equations (3.20). Hence, for a plate of constant thickness, the theory of plane stress as developed in the preceding chapter carries over without changes. However, we have to find equations for the bending quantities m_x, m_y, m_{xy}, and w.

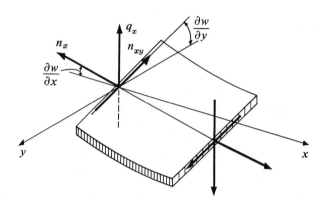

Figure 4.2

By taking moments about the y- and x-axis, of all forces acting on the element (Figure 4.1), and remembering that stress resultants acting on opposite faces differ by quantities of the form $(\partial m_x/\partial x)\,dx$, $(\partial m_y/\partial y)\,dy$, etc., we obtain

$$\frac{\partial m_x}{\partial x} + \frac{\partial m_{yx}}{\partial y} = q_x, \qquad \frac{\partial m_{xy}}{\partial x} + \frac{\partial m_y}{\partial y} = q_y. \qquad (4.11)$$

In setting up the last of the equilibrium equations by equating the sum of all forces acting in the z-direction to zero, we must consider the following fact. Due to the slope of the deflected element, the membrane forces will have components in the vertical direction† (Figure 4.2). Along the face

---

† Although the present theory is restricted to small deflections and small slopes, these components may be of importance if the membrane forces are large.

whose coordinate is x these components are

$$-\left(n_x \frac{\partial w}{\partial x} + n_{xy} \frac{\partial w}{\partial y}\right) dy.$$

Along the opposite face with coordinate $x + dx$ they are

$$\left(n_x \frac{\partial w}{\partial x} + n_{xy} \frac{\partial w}{\partial y}\right) dy + \frac{\partial}{\partial x}\left(n_x \frac{\partial w}{\partial x} + n_{xy} \frac{\partial w}{\partial y}\right) dy\, dx.$$

Similar contributions come from the two faces y and $y + dy$. Adding up, we have

$$\left[n_x \frac{\partial^2 w}{\partial x^2} + 2n_{xy} \frac{\partial^2 w}{\partial x \partial y} + n_y \frac{\partial^2 w}{\partial y^2} + \left(\frac{\partial n_x}{\partial x} + \frac{\partial n_{yx}}{\partial y}\right)\frac{\partial w}{\partial x} \right.$$
$$\left. + \left(\frac{\partial n_{xy}}{\partial x} + \frac{\partial n_y}{\partial y}\right)\frac{\partial w}{\partial y} \right] dx\, dy.$$

The last two terms vanish by virtue of Equations (4.10). Together with the contributions from the shearing forces q_x and q_y, we obtain, after adding a distributed normal load of intensity p,

$$\frac{\partial q_x}{\partial x} + \frac{\partial q_y}{\partial y} + n_x \frac{\partial^2 w}{\partial x^2} + 2n_{xy} \frac{\partial^2 w}{\partial x \partial y} + n_y \frac{\partial^2 w}{\partial y^2} + p = 0. \qquad (4.12)$$

4.3. Differential Equation for the Deflection

Substitution of Equations (4.6) into Equations (4.11) results in (if constant thickness of the plate is supposed),

$$\left.\begin{aligned}
q_x &= -K \frac{\partial}{\partial x} [\nabla^2 w + (1 + \nu)\alpha m_\Theta], \\
q_y &= -K \frac{\partial}{\partial y} [\nabla^2 w + (1 + \nu)\alpha m_\Theta].
\end{aligned}\right\} \qquad (4.13)$$

Equations (4.12) and (4.13) may now be combined to give

$$K\nabla^2\nabla^2 w = p - (1 + \nu)K\alpha\nabla^2 m_\Theta + n_x \frac{\partial^2 w}{\partial x^2} + 2n_{xy} \frac{\partial^2 w}{\partial x \partial y} + n_y \frac{\partial^2 w}{\partial y^2}. \quad (4.14)$$

The last three terms on the right-hand side of the equation represent the influence of the membrane forces on the deflection. If these forces are small, the terms may be ignored.

4.4. Boundary Conditions

The boundary conditions of the membrane forces n_x, n_{xy}, n_y have been discussed in the preceding chapter, p. 27 ff. For the bending problem, four basic types of edge conditions may be distinguished.

Clamped edge

Both deflection and slope normal to the boundary are zero,

$$w = 0, \qquad \frac{\partial w}{\partial n} \equiv \frac{\partial w}{\partial x} \cos \alpha + \frac{\partial w}{\partial y} \sin \alpha = 0, \qquad (4.15)$$

where α is the angle between the normal n and the direction of x (Figure 4.3).

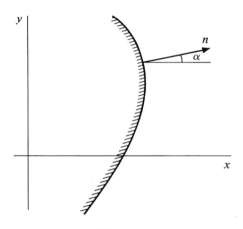

Figure 4.3

The two boundary conditions of Equations (4.15) refer to displacement and slope of the plate and are, therefore, *kinematic conditions*.

Simply supported edge

Deflection and bending moment vanish,

$$w = 0, \qquad m_n = m_x \cos^2 \alpha + m_{xy} \sin 2\alpha + m_y \sin^2 \alpha = 0, \qquad (4.16)$$

m_x, m_{xy}, m_y are given in terms of w by Equations (4.6).

Of the two boundary conditions given in Equations (4.16), the first is kinematic while the second, which refers to the bending moment, is a *dynamic condition*.

Free edge

Equation (4.14) is of fourth order in w. Hence, only two boundary conditions can be satisfied along the edges of the plate while, for a real plate, the three quantities m_n, m_{ns}, and q_n would have to vanish at a free edge. This discrepancy is due to assumption (1) of Section 4.1 which states that the plate is supposed to be rigid in shear. The difficulty has been overcome by Kirchhoff who derived the following conditions for a free edge:†

$$m_n = 0, \qquad q_n + \frac{\partial m_{ns}}{\partial s} = 0, \qquad (4.17)$$

where

$$q_n = q_x \cos \alpha + q_y \sin \alpha, \qquad m_{ns} = -\frac{m_x - m_y}{2} \sin 2\alpha + m_{xy} \cos 2\alpha.$$

Utilizing Equations (4.11), the second of relations (4.17) may be written as

$$\frac{\partial m_n}{\partial n} + 2 \frac{\partial m_{ns}}{\partial s} = 0,$$

or, after substitution from Equations (4.6),

$$-K \frac{\partial}{\partial n}\left[\frac{\partial^2 w}{\partial n^2} + (2 - \nu)\frac{\partial^2 w}{\partial s^2}\right] = 0. \qquad (4.18)$$

If we wish to take the contribution of the membrane forces into account, we have to replace Equation (4.18) by

$$-K \frac{\partial}{\partial n}\left[\frac{\partial^2 w}{\partial n^2} + (2 - \nu)\frac{\partial^2 w}{\partial s^2}\right] + n_n \frac{\partial w}{\partial n} + n_{ns} \frac{\partial w}{\partial s} = 0. \qquad (4.19)$$

Both boundary conditions of Equations (4.17) are of the dynamic type. For future use, we note the two formulas

$$\left.\begin{aligned}\frac{\partial}{\partial s} &= \frac{\partial}{\partial y} \cos \alpha - \frac{\partial}{\partial x} \sin \alpha, \\[2mm] \frac{\partial}{\partial n} &= \frac{\partial}{\partial y} \sin \alpha + \frac{\partial}{\partial x} \cos \alpha.\end{aligned}\right\} \qquad (4.20)$$

Elastically restrained edge

If the rotation $\partial w/\partial n$ at the edge of the plate is resisted by a moment $\gamma \partial w/\partial n$ per unit length, we have the boundary condition

$$m_n = \gamma \frac{\partial w}{\partial n}. \qquad (4.21)$$

† See, for instance, reference [17].

If the edge is elastically supported against deflection by a spring force cw per unit length, the boundary condition

$$q_n + \frac{\partial m_{ns}}{\partial s} = -cw \tag{4.22}$$

has to be satisfied.

4.5. Two Simple Cases

Consider a plate of arbitrary planform. When the temperature is independent of x and y (n_Θ and m_Θ are constant), and the plate is either free or clamped along its entire edge, a simple set of formulas results.

Free plate

Upon putting $n_x = n_y = n_{xy} = 0$ in Equations (4.5) and $m_x = m_y = m_{xy} = 0$ in Equations (4.6), we get

$$\varepsilon_{xx}^0 = \varepsilon_{yy}^0 = \alpha n_\Theta, \qquad \varepsilon_{xy}^0 = 0,$$

and

$$\frac{\partial^2 w}{\partial x^2} = \frac{\partial^2 w}{\partial y^2} = \alpha m_\Theta, \qquad \frac{\partial^2 w}{\partial x \partial y} = 0.$$

Hence,

$$w = -\frac{\alpha m_\Theta}{2}(x^2 + y^2).$$

This solution satisfies Equation (4.14), with $p = 0$, and the boundary conditions of Equations (4.18).

The plate will remain plane if $m_\Theta = 0$, that is, if the temperature is symmetric with respect to the midplane $z = 0$.

If the plate is *circular*, its edge line $x^2 + y^2 = R^2$ will, after bending, still lie in a plane. Hence, the solution is also valid for the simply supported circular plate.

From Equations (4.9), we note

$$\sigma_{xx} = \sigma_{yy} = \frac{E\alpha}{1 - \nu}(n_\Theta - \Theta + zm_\Theta), \qquad \sigma_{xy} = 0$$

for the stresses in the plate. This leaves a self-equilibrating system of stresses at the edge. According to Saint-Venant's principle, the influence of these stresses will be confined to the proximity of the edges.

Clamped plate

The deflection is now zero everywhere, $w \equiv 0$. This solution satisfies Equations (4.14) and (4.15) while, from Equations (4.6), we find

$$m_x = m_y = -(1 + \nu)K\alpha m_\Theta, \qquad m_{xy} = 0.$$

Hence, from Equations (4.9),

$$\sigma_{xx} = \frac{n_x}{h} + \frac{E\alpha}{1 - \nu}(n_\Theta - \Theta), \qquad \sigma_{yy} = \frac{n_y}{h} + \frac{E\alpha}{1 - \nu}(n_\Theta - \Theta), \qquad \sigma_{xy} = \frac{n_{xy}}{h}.$$

If the plate is free to expand in its midplane, $n_x = n_y = n_{xy} = 0$. If, on the other hand, the plate is held fixed along its entire edge,

$$\varepsilon^0_{xx} = \varepsilon^0_{yy} = \varepsilon^0_{xy} = 0, \qquad n_x = n_y = -(1 + \nu)\alpha D n_\Theta, \qquad n_{xy} = 0.$$

4.6. Axisymmetric Bending of a Circular Plate

If the temperature varies across the thickness and along the radial coordinate r, but is independent of the polar angle θ, Equation (4.14) takes on the form

$$K\nabla^2\nabla^2 w = p - (1 + \nu)K\alpha\nabla^2 m_\Theta + \frac{1}{r}\frac{d}{dr}\left(r n_r \frac{dw}{dr}\right), \qquad (4.23)$$

where

$$\nabla^2 w = \frac{d^2 w}{dr^2} + \frac{1}{r}\frac{dw}{dr} = \frac{1}{r}\frac{d}{dr}\left(r\frac{dw}{dr}\right).$$

Equation (4.23) may be obtained by observing that the contribution of the membrane forces to equilibrium in the vertical direction is now equal to

$$-n_r \frac{dw}{dr} r \, d\theta.$$

Therefore, Equation (4.12) is to be replaced by

$$\frac{d}{dr}\left(r q_r + r n_r \frac{dw}{dr}\right) + pr = 0. \qquad (4.24)$$

Equations (4.11) become

$$\frac{dm_r}{dr} + \frac{m_r - m_\theta}{r} = q_r, \qquad (4.25)$$

and the bending moments are

$$m_r = -K\left[\frac{d^2w}{dr^2} + \frac{\nu}{r}\frac{dw}{dr} + (1 + \nu)\alpha m_\Theta\right], \left.\begin{array}{l}\\ \\ \\ \\ \end{array}\right\}$$

$$m_\theta = -K\left[\frac{1}{r}\frac{dw}{dr} + \nu\frac{d^2w}{dr^2} + (1 + \nu)\alpha m_\Theta\right].$$

(4.26)

Substitution of Equations (4.25) and (4.26) into Equation (4.24) gives Equation (4.23).

If membrane forces are absent or sufficiently small to be neglected in Equation (4.23), the general solution with $p = 0$ is

$$w = (1 + \nu)\alpha\left[C_1 + C_2 r^2 + C_3 \log\frac{r}{a} + C_4 r^2 \log\frac{r}{a} + \int_r^a \frac{H(r)}{r}\, dr\right], \quad (4.27)$$

where a is the outer radius of the plate and

$$H(r) = \int_b^r m_\Theta(r)r\, dr. \quad (4.28)$$

Here, b is the inner radius in case the plate has a hole, while $b = 0$ for the solid plate.

The bending moments are obtained from Equations (4.26),

$$m_r = -(1 + \nu)\alpha K\left[2(1 + \nu)C_2 - (1 - \nu)\frac{C_3}{r^2} + (3 + \nu)C_4\right.$$

$$\left. + 2(1 + \nu)C_4 \log\frac{r}{a} + \frac{1 - \nu}{r^2}H\right], \left.\begin{array}{l}\\ \\ \\ \\ \\ \\ \\ \\ \end{array}\right\}$$

$$m_\theta = -(1 + \nu)\alpha K\left[2(1 + \nu)C_2 + (1 - \nu)\frac{C_3}{r^2} + (1 + 3\nu)C_4\right.$$

$$\left. + 2(1 + \nu)C_4 \log\frac{r}{a} - \frac{1 - \nu}{r^2}H + (1 - \nu)m_\Theta\right],$$

(4.29)

$$m_{r\theta} = 0.$$

The shearing force is

$$q_r = -K\frac{d}{dr}[\nabla^2 w + (1 + \nu)\alpha m_\Theta] = -4(1 + \nu)aK\frac{C_4}{r}. \quad (4.30)$$

The constants of integration $C_1, \ldots, C_4$ are to be determined from the boundary conditions at the inner and outer edge of the annular plate. In order to avoid singularities at $r = 0$, the constants C_3 and C_4 must be equal to zero for a solid plate. The shearing force then vanishes throughout the plate (load $p = 0$!).

Solid plate, simply supported

Putting $w = 0$ and $m_r = 0$ along $r = a$, one obtains

$$C_1 = -a^2 C_2 = \frac{1 - \nu}{2(1 + \nu)} H(a).$$ (4.31)

Solid plate, clamped

The boundary conditions $w = 0$ and $dw/dr = 0$ on $r = a$ yield

$$C_1 = -a^2 C_2 = -\tfrac{1}{2} H(a).$$ (4.32)

4.7. Influence Function Method

If in Maysel's formula [see Equation (2.46)], the point P is chosen on the midplane of the plate, one may write

$$w(x, y) = \alpha \int_A \left[\int_{-h/2}^{+h/2} \Theta(\xi, \eta, \zeta) \bar{s}(\xi, \eta, \zeta, x, y) \, d\zeta \right] dA,$$

where $dA = d\xi \, d\eta$ is an element of the midplane area A, and $\bar{s}$ is the sum of the normal stresses at point ξ, η, ζ, due to a concentrated unit force acting in the direction of z at point x, y, 0. From Equations (4.9) with $\bar{\sigma}_{zz} = 0$,

$$\bar{s} = \frac{12}{h^3} \zeta [\bar{m}_x(\xi, \eta, x, y) + \bar{m}_y(\xi, \eta, x, y)].$$

Substituting this into the equation above, integrating over ζ, and utilizing Equation (4.8), we find

$$w(x, y) = \alpha \iint_A m_\Theta(\xi, \eta) \bar{m}(\xi, \eta, x, y) \, d\xi \, d\eta,$$ (4.33)

where $\bar{m} = \bar{m}_x + \bar{m}_y$.

Equation (4.33) is particularly useful for engineering applications. A vast literature exists on the *influence functions* $\bar{m}_x$ and $\bar{m}_y$ due to a single concentrated load $P = 1$ for a variety of planforms and edge conditions.† The connection between the deflection $\bar{w}$ and the moment $\bar{m}$ is from Equation (4.6),

$$\bar{m}(\xi, \eta, x, y) = -(1 + \nu)K\left[\frac{\partial^2 \bar{w}(\xi, \eta, x, y)}{\partial \xi^2} + \frac{\partial^2 \bar{w}(\xi, \eta, x, y)}{\partial \eta^2} \right].$$ (4.34)

---

† See, for instance, Section 28.6 of *Handbook of Engineering Mechanics*, ed. W. Flügge (New York: McGraw-Hill Book Co., 1962), where additional literature may be found.

As an example, we mention the influence function for an *infinite plate*,

$$\bar{m} = -\frac{1+\nu}{2\pi}\log s, \qquad s = \sqrt{(x-\xi)^2 + (y-\eta)^2}, \qquad (4.35)$$

and for a *rectangular plate* simply supported along all four edges $x = 0$, a and $y = 0$, b

$$\bar{m} = 2(1+\nu)\sum_{n=1}^{\infty} \sin \alpha_n x \sin \alpha_n \xi \frac{\sinh \alpha_n(b-y) \sinh \alpha_n \eta}{\alpha_n a \sinh \alpha_n b}, \quad 0 \leqslant \eta \leqslant y,$$

$$\bar{m} = 2(1+\nu)\sum_{n=1}^{\infty} \sin \alpha_n x \sin \alpha_n \xi \frac{\sinh \alpha_n y \sinh \alpha_n(b-\eta)}{\alpha_n a \sinh \alpha_n b}, \quad y \leqslant \eta \leqslant b,$$

$$(4.36)$$

where $\alpha_n = \dfrac{n\pi}{a}$.

4.8. Hot Area in an Infinite Plate†

A rectangular region $|x| \leqslant a$, $|y| \leqslant b$ in an infinite plate is heated to a constant temperature moment $m_\Theta = C$. Outside of that region, the temperature remains unchanged. The bending and twisting moments in the plate are to be determined.

We use Equations (4.33) and (4.35):

$$w(x, y) = -\frac{1+\nu}{4\pi}\alpha C \int_{-a}^{+a} d\xi \int_{-b}^{+b} \log\left[(x-\xi)^2 + (y-\eta)^2\right] d\eta.$$

Differentiating under the integral sign, we find

$$\frac{\partial w}{\partial x} = -\frac{1+\nu}{4\pi}\alpha C \int_{-a}^{+a} d\xi \int_{-b}^{+b} \frac{2(x-\xi)}{(x-\xi)^2 + (y-\eta)^2} d\eta$$

$$= \frac{1+\nu}{4\pi}\alpha C \int_{-b}^{+b} \log \frac{(x-a)^2 + (y-\eta)^2}{(x+a)^2 + (y-\eta)^2} d\eta.$$

Differentiating once more, and integrating,

$$\frac{\partial^2 w}{\partial x^2} = \frac{1+\nu}{2\pi}\alpha C\left[\tan^{-1}\frac{y+b}{x-a} + \tan^{-1}\frac{y-b}{x+a}\right.$$

$$\left. - \tan^{-1}\frac{y+b}{x+a} - \tan^{-1}\frac{y-b}{x-a}\right]. \quad (4.37)$$

---

† See reference [10], p. 446.

Similarly,

$$\frac{\partial^2 w}{\partial y^2} = \frac{1+\nu}{2\pi} \alpha C \left[\tan^{-1} \frac{x-a}{y+b} + \tan^{-1} \frac{x+a}{y-b} \right.$$

$$\left. - \tan^{-1} \frac{x+a}{y+b} - \tan^{-1} \frac{x-a}{y-b} \right], \quad (4.38)$$

$$\frac{\partial^2 w}{\partial x \partial y} = \frac{1+\nu}{4\pi} \alpha C \log \left[\frac{(x-a)^2 + (y-b)^2 \, (x+a)^2 + (y-b)^2}{(x-a)^2 + (y+b)^2 \, (x+a)^2 + (y+b)^2} \right], \quad (4.39)$$

where principal values of the inverse trigonometric function are to be taken, that is,

$$-\frac{\pi}{2} < \tan^{-1} \alpha < \frac{\pi}{2}.$$

Substitution of Equations (4.37) through (4.39) into Equations (4.6) gives the desired moments.

We note that if we cross the sides $x = a$ of the hot region, $x - a$ changes sign and a jump of magnitude π in $\tan^{-1}[(y+b)/(x-a)]$ and $\tan^{-1}[(y-b)/(x-a)]$ occurs. Thus, $\partial^2 w/\partial x^2$ is discontinuous on $x = \pm a$. Similarly, $\partial^2 w/\partial y^2$ experiences a discontinuity on $y = \pm b$. On the boundary of the hot region, the bending moments are, therefore, discontinuous. Using

$$\tan^{-1} \alpha + \tan^{-1} \frac{1}{\alpha} = \begin{cases} \dfrac{\pi}{2} & \alpha > 0, \\[2ex] -\dfrac{\pi}{2} & \alpha < 0, \end{cases}$$

we get for the sum:

$$m_x + m_y = \begin{cases} -(1-\nu^2) K \alpha C, & \text{inside the hot area}, \\ 0, & \text{outside the hot area}. \end{cases} \quad (4.40)$$

At the corners $x = \pm a$, $y = \pm b$ of the rectangle the mixed derivative $\partial^2 w/\partial x \partial y$ and, hence, the twisting moment take on infinite values.

If we let the hot area A shrink to zero while, at the same time, let the temperature increase in such a manner that $\lim_{A \to 0} A m_\Theta = \kappa \neq 0$, we obtain a so-called *bending hot spot*. Equations (4.33) and (4.35) give, in this case,

$$w(x, y) = -\frac{1+\nu}{2\pi} \alpha \kappa \log r, \qquad r = \sqrt{x^2 + y^2}. \quad (4.41)$$

4.9. Rectangular Plate with Two Parallel Edges Simply Supported

A rectangular plate is subject to an arbitrary temperature distribution. Two parallel edges, $x = 0$ and $x = a$ are simply supported while the other two are supported in any manner. We assume the membrane forces, if any, to be sufficiently small so that their influence on bending may be neglected.

The method of influence functions is, of course, available in this case. A different procedure consists in solving Equation (4.14) directly. A convenient method for doing this has been developed by Mindlin and Goodman, and has been applied to the present case by Das and Navaratna.†

The solution of Equation (4.14), which now takes the form,

$$\nabla^2\nabla^2 w + (1 + \nu)\alpha\nabla^2 m_\Theta = 0,\qquad(4.42)$$

is assumed to be

$$w(x, y) = (1 + \nu)\alpha[U(x, y) + m_\Theta(0, y)H_0(x) + m_\Theta(a, y)H_1(x)].\quad(4.43)$$

The functions $H_0(x)$ and $H_1(x)$ are selected to give homogeneous boundary conditions on $U(x, y)$ in $x = 0, a$. In the present case, we have, from Equations (4.16),

$$w = 0,\qquad m_x = 0,$$

$$\text{or}\qquad w = 0,\qquad \frac{\partial^2 w}{\partial x^2} + (1 + \nu)\alpha m_\Theta = 0 \qquad \text{along} \qquad x = 0, a.$$

This results from Equation (4.6) since, with $w \equiv 0$ along $x = \text{const.}$, it follows that $\partial^2 w/\partial y^2 \equiv 0$ there. We let, therefore,

$$H_0(x) = \frac{a^2}{6}\left[2\frac{x}{a} - 3\left(\frac{x}{a}\right)^2 + \left(\frac{x}{a}\right)^3\right],\qquad H_1(x) = \frac{a^2}{6}\left[\frac{x}{a} - \left(\frac{x}{a}\right)^3\right].\quad(4.44)$$

Substitution into Equation (4.42) gives the boundary value problem

$$\left.\begin{array}{c}\nabla^2\nabla^2 U(x, y) + F(x, y) = 0,\\[4pt] U = 0,\qquad \partial^2 U/\partial x^2 = 0 \qquad \text{on} \qquad x = 0, a,\end{array}\right\}\qquad(4.45)$$

where

$$F(x, y) = \nabla^2 m_\Theta(x, y) + \frac{\partial^4 m_\Theta(0, y)}{\partial y^4}H_0(x) + 2\frac{\partial^2 m_\Theta(0, y)}{\partial y^2}H_0''(x)$$

$$+ \frac{\partial^4 m_\Theta(a, y)}{\partial y^4}H_1(x) + 2\frac{\partial^2 m_\Theta(a, y)}{\partial y^2}H_1''(x),\quad(4.46)$$

with

$$H_0''(x) = \frac{x}{a} - 1,\qquad H_1''(x) = -\frac{x}{a}.\qquad(4.47)$$

† See reference [18].

The solution of Equation (4.45) is

$$
\left.
\begin{aligned}
U(x, y) &= \sum_{n=1}^{\infty} Y_n(y) \sin \alpha_n x, \\[2mm]
Y_n(y) &= \frac{1}{\alpha_n^2} [(A_n + \alpha_n y B_n) \cosh \alpha_n y \\
&\qquad\qquad + (C_n + \alpha_n y D_n) \sinh \alpha_n y] - L_n(y),
\end{aligned}
\right\} \tag{4.48}
$$

where

$$
\left.
\begin{aligned}
L_n(y) &= e^{-\alpha_n y} \int dy \int e^{2\alpha_n y} \, dy \int dy \int e^{-\alpha_n y} F_n(y) \, dy, \\[2mm]
\alpha_n &= \frac{n\pi}{a}.
\end{aligned}
\right\} \tag{4.49}
$$

The $F_n(y)$ are the Fourier coefficients of $F(x, y)$:

$$
F_n(y) = \frac{2}{a} \int_0^a F(x, y) \sin \alpha_n x \, dx. \tag{4.50}
$$

The constants A_n, B_n, C_n, and D_n are to be determined from the boundary conditions along the edges $y = 0$ and $y = b$.

For convenience, we note the derivatives needed in the evaluation of Equations (4.6):

$$
\left.
\begin{aligned}
\frac{\partial^2 U}{\partial x^2} &= -\sum [(A_n + \alpha_n y B_n) \cosh \alpha_n y \\
&\qquad + (C_n + \alpha_n y D_n) \sinh \alpha_n y - \alpha_n^2 L_n(y)] \sin \alpha_n x, \\
\frac{\partial^2 U}{\partial y^2} &= \sum [(A_n + 2D_n + \alpha_n y B_n) \cosh \alpha_n y \\
&\qquad + (C_n + 2B_n + \alpha_n y D_n) \sinh \alpha_n y - L_n''(y)] \sin \alpha_n x, \\
\frac{\partial^2 U}{\partial x \, \partial y} &= \sum [(A_n + D_n + \alpha_n y B_n) \sinh \alpha_n y \\
&\qquad + (C_n + B_n + \alpha_n y D_n) \cosh \alpha_n y - \alpha_n L_n'(y)] \cos \alpha_n x, \\
L_n'(y) &= -\alpha_n L_n(y) + e^{-\alpha_n y} \int e^{2\alpha_n y} \, dy \int dy \int e^{-\alpha_n y} F_n(y) \, dy, \\
L_n''(y) &= -\alpha_n^2 L_n(y) - 2\alpha_n L_n'(y) + e^{\alpha_n y} \int dy \int e^{-\alpha_n y} F_n(y) \, dy.
\end{aligned}
\right\} \tag{4.51}
$$

As an example, we consider the case where the plate is simply supported along $y = 0$, and is clamped along $y = b$. The temperature moment is assumed constant over the entire plate, $m_\Theta = M = $ const.

We have the boundary conditions

$$w = 0, \qquad m_y = 0,$$

or $w = 0, \qquad \dfrac{\partial^2 w}{\partial y^2} + (1 + \nu)\alpha M = 0$ along $y = 0,$

$$w = 0, \qquad \dfrac{\partial w}{\partial y} = 0 \qquad \text{along} \qquad y = b.$$

In terms of U, this reads, from Equation (4.43),

$$\begin{aligned} U &= -M[H_0(x) + H_1(x)], & \partial^2 U/\partial y^2 &= -M & \text{along} \quad y = 0, \\ U &= -M[H_0(x) + H_1(x)], & \partial U/\partial y &= 0 & \text{along} \quad y = b. \end{aligned} \right\}$$

(4.52)

Transforming the right-hand sides into Fourier series, we have

$$-M[H_0(x) + H_1(x)] = -M\frac{a^2}{2}\left[\frac{x}{a} - \left(\frac{x}{a}\right)^2\right] = \sum a_n \sin \alpha_n x,$$

with

$$a_n = \frac{2}{a}\int_0^a U(x, 0)\sin \alpha_n x\, dx = \begin{cases} 0, & n \text{ even}, \\ -\dfrac{4M}{a\alpha_n^3}, & n \text{ odd}, \end{cases}$$

and, similarly,

$$-M = \sum b_n \sin \alpha_n x, \qquad b_n = \begin{cases} 0, & n \text{ even} \\ -\dfrac{4M}{a\alpha_n}, & n \text{ odd} \end{cases} \right\} = \alpha_n^2 a_n.$$

Since $F(x, y) = 0$ in the present case we have $L_n(y) = 0$. Substituting Equation (4.48) into the boundary conditions, Equations (4.52), and comparing coefficients, one obtains the following four equations for the constants $A_n, \ldots, D_n$:

$$\left. \begin{aligned} &A_n = \alpha_n^2 a_n, \\ &(A_n + \alpha_n b B_n)\cosh \alpha_n b + (C_n + \alpha_n b D_n)\sinh \alpha_n b = \alpha_n a_n^2, \\ &A_n + 2D_n = b_n, \\ &(A_n + D_n + \alpha_n b B_n)\sinh \alpha_n b \\ &\qquad\qquad + (C_n + B_n + \alpha_n b D_n)\cosh \alpha_n b = 0. \end{aligned} \right\}$$

(4.53)

For n even, all constants vanish, while for n odd, we get

$$
\left.
\begin{aligned}
A_n &= -\frac{4M}{n\pi}, \\[2mm]
B_n &= 2A_n \frac{\cosh \alpha_n b - 1}{2\alpha_n b - \sinh 2\alpha_n b}, \\[2mm]
C_n &= 2A_n \frac{(\sinh \alpha_n b - \alpha_n b)\sinh \alpha_n b}{2\alpha_n b - \sinh 2\alpha_n b} - B_n, \\[2mm]
D_n &= 0.
\end{aligned}
\right\} \qquad (n = 1, 3, 5, \ldots) \quad (4.54)
$$

So far, the solution is purely formal. To verify it, uniform convergence of the series of Equations (4.48) and its derivatives has to be established. Using the asymptotic values

$$
B_n \sim -2A_n e^{-\alpha_n b} = \frac{8M}{a\alpha_n} e^{-\alpha_n b}, \qquad C_n \sim -A_n - B_n,
$$

one finds

$$
Y_n(y) \sim \frac{4M}{a\alpha_n^3} (\alpha_n y - 1) e^{-\alpha_n(b-y)}.
$$

Hence, the series of Equations (4.48) converges, together with all derivatives, in the half-open interval $[0, b)$. The differential equation (4.45) in the interior of the plate and the boundary conditions along the three edges $x = 0$, a and $y = 0$ are, therefore, satisfied. On $y = b$, we have uniform convergence of U and its first derivatives, and the boundary conditions are satisfied there too. However, the series expansions for the bending and twisting moments diverge along the edge $y = b$.

4.10. Thermal Buckling

If the membrane stresses due to a mean temperature distribution $n_\Theta(x, y)$ in a plate are compressive and are sufficiently large, equilibrium may become unstable, and out-of-plane buckling may occur without any external forces being present. This phenomenon is termed "thermal buckling."

Even if the membrane forces are not large enough to cause buckling, they still will produce a reduction in the apparent bending stiffness of the plate. As a consequence, external buckling loads, as well as natural frequencies of flexural vibrations, will be lowered. If the apparent stiffness drops to zero, thermal buckling will occur.

Equation (4.14) represents the influence of the membrane forces n_x, n_{xy}, n_y on the deflection w and may, therefore, be used to determine the reduction in natural frequencies or the buckling temperature.

Let $n_\Theta(x, y)$ be the given mean temperature distribution with $m_\Theta \equiv 0$, and let n_x, n_{xy}, n_y be the corresponding membrane forces obtained by the methods of Chapter 3. The equation of the vibrating plate follows from Equation (4.14) if we replace p by the inertial force $-\rho h \partial^2 w/\partial t^2$ per unit area of the midplane. Putting, now,

$$w(x, y, t) = W(x, y)e^{i\omega t},$$

with ω as the unknown natural frequency, and substituting, one gets

$$K\nabla^2\nabla^2 W - \rho h\omega^2 W - n_x\frac{\partial^2 W}{\partial x^2} - 2n_{xy}\frac{\partial^2 W}{\partial x \partial y} - n_y\frac{\partial^2 W}{\partial y^2} = 0, \quad (4.55)$$

together with the corresponding boundary conditions. We have thus obtained an *eigenvalue problem*, and we have to find those values of ω^2 for which Equation (4.55) possesses a nontrivial solution.

Similarly, if we want to know whether or not a given mean temperature $n_\Theta(x, y)$ with membrane forces n_x, n_{xy}, n_y is critical, i.e., may produce thermal buckling, we replace it by $\lambda n_\Theta(x, y)$ with membrane forces raised to λn_x, λn_{xy}, λn_y. The plate will then be in danger of buckling if λ corresponds, in absolute value, to the smallest eigenvalue of the equation

$$K\nabla^2\nabla^2 w - \lambda\left(n_x\frac{\partial^2 w}{\partial x^2} + 2n_{xy}\frac{\partial^2 w}{\partial x \partial y} + n_y\frac{\partial^2 w}{\partial y^2}\right) = 0 \quad (4.56)$$

with the appropriate boundary conditions adjoined. In particular, the given mean temperature distribution $n_\Theta(x, y)$ will be critical if the smallest eigenvalue is $\lambda = 1$.

Since, in contrast to ordinary buckling problems, the membrane forces n_x, n_{xy}, n_y in either Equation (4.55) or (4.56) are not constants, but functions of x, y, it is, in general, not possible to find exact solutions. Of the approximate procedures available, the *Ritz-Galerkin method* discussed in the following is probably the most frequently used.[†]

The solution of Equation (4.55) or (4.56) is approximated by a finite series

$$w(x, y) = \sum_{n=1}^{N} A_n\varphi_n(x, y), \quad (4.57)$$

where $\varphi_n(x, y)$ are suitably chosen functions, i.e., functions which satisfy the kinematic, but not necessarily the dynamic boundary conditions.[‡] The A_n are arbitrary coefficients.

---

† See reference [19].
‡ The approximation is, of course, considerably improved if both conditions are satisfied.

If we write the two equations (4.55) and (4.56) in the general form $L[w] = 0$ and substitute Equation (4.57), we find that, in general, the equations are not satisfied. The error $L[w] \neq 0$ may be considered as a fictitious load p acting on the plate,

$$p = L[w] \tag{4.58}$$

and may be minimized, together with fictitious edge loads from Equations (4.6) and (4.19),

$$m = -K\left(\frac{\partial^2 w}{\partial n^2} + v\frac{\partial^2 w}{\partial s^2}\right), \tag{4.59}$$

$$q = -K\frac{\partial}{\partial n}\left[\frac{\partial^2 w}{\partial n^2} + (2 - v)\frac{\partial^2 w}{\partial s^2}\right] + n_n\frac{\partial w}{\partial n} + n_{ns}\frac{\partial w}{\partial s}, \tag{4.60}$$

by applying the principle of virtual displacements

$$\iint_A p\delta w \, dx \, dy - \oint_B m\delta\left(\frac{\partial w}{\partial n}\right) ds + \oint_B q\delta w \, ds = 0.$$

Since the functions φ_n in Equation (4.57) are prescribed, we have

$$\delta w = \sum_{n=1}^{N} \varphi_n \delta A_n.$$

The δA_n are arbitrary and independent of each other. Hence, the following set of N equations, homogeneous and linear in the A_n, is obtained

$$\iint_A L[w]\varphi_i \, dx \, dy - \oint_B m\frac{\partial\varphi_i}{\partial n} ds + \oint_B q\varphi_i \, ds = 0$$
$$(i = 1, 2, \ldots, N). \tag{4.61}$$

Integration is to be extended over the midplane area A and along the boundary B of the plate. Here, δw is zero at an edge, simply supported or clamped, and $\delta(\partial w/\partial n)$ vanishes at a clamped edge. Hence, the second boundary integral is zero along a simply supported edge while both boundary integrals are absent at a clamped edge.

Equations (4.61) have a nontrivial solution $A_n \neq 0$ if and only if their determinant vanishes. This furnishes the eigenvalues ω^2 or λ, as the case may be.

A number of solutions of thermal buckling problems is available in the literature.†

---

† See, for instance, references [19] and [20].

4.11. Example: Rectangular Plate

We now apply the Ritz-Galerkin method to a rectangular plate, $0 \leqslant x \leqslant a$, $0 \leqslant y \leqslant b$, simply supported along all four edges and subject to a system of symmetric thermal membrane forces given by†

$$n_x = - \frac{\pi^2 K}{b^2}\left(1 + \sum_{k=1,3,5} p_k \sin \frac{k \pi y}{b}\right), \qquad n_y = n_{xy} = 0, \qquad (4.62)$$

where p_k are nondimensional Fourier coefficients.

The functions

$$\varphi_n = \sin \frac{n \pi y}{b} \sin \frac{s \pi x}{a} \qquad (n = 1, 3, 5, \ldots)$$

satisfy both the kinematic and dynamic boundary conditions. Here, s is some as yet undetermined integer. Hence, $m = 0$ in Equation (4.61) and we have, upon substituting $L(w)$ from Equation (4.56),

$$\int_0^a dx \int_0^b \left[\nabla^2\nabla^2 w + \lambda \frac{\pi^2}{b^2}\left(1 + \sum p_k \sin \frac{k\pi y}{b}\right)\frac{\partial^2 w}{\partial x^2}\right]\varphi_n \, dy = 0.$$

For the sake of simplicity, we restrict ourselves to a one-term expansion

$$w = A \sin \frac{\pi y}{b} \sin \frac{s \pi x}{a}. \qquad (4.63)$$

Then,

$$\frac{\partial^2 w}{\partial x^2} = - \frac{\pi^2 \mu^2}{b^2}\,w, \qquad \nabla^2 w = - \frac{\pi^2}{b^2}(1 + \mu^2)w, \qquad \nabla^2\nabla^2 w = \frac{\pi^4}{b^4}(1 + \mu^2)^2 w,$$

where

$$\mu = s \frac{b}{a}.$$

It follows that

$$\int_0^b \left[(1 + \mu^2)^2 - \lambda \mu^2\left(1 + \sum p_k \sin \frac{k\pi y}{b}\right)\right]\left(\sin \frac{\pi y}{b}\right)^2 dy = 0,$$

or, after integration,

$$\frac{1}{\lambda} = \left(\frac{\mu}{1 + \mu^2}\right)^2\left\{1 - \frac{8}{\pi}\sum_{k=1,3,5}\frac{p_k}{k(k^2 - 4)}\right\}. \qquad (4.64)$$

---

† See reference [19].

The value of μ is determined by making λ as small as possible. This gives $\mu = 1$. Since s must be an integer, it is selected to bring μ as close to unity as possible.

The temperature distribution becomes critical if the membrane forces reach the value λn_x.

The accuracy of the solution can be improved by taking more terms in the series for w. This will be left as an exercise.

• *Problems*

1. Derive Equations (4.9).

HINT: Solve Equations (4.3) for the stress components and substitute ε_{ij}^0 and w from Equations (4.5) and (4.6).

2. Determine the circumferential stress $\sigma_{\theta\theta}$ at the edge $r = a$ of a solid circular plate simply supported and subject to a temperature $\Theta(r, z)$.

HINT: Substitute Equation (4.31) into Equation (4.29) and use Equation (4.9) to get

$$\sigma_{\theta\theta}\big|_{r=a} = \frac{n_\theta}{h} + E\alpha z\left[\frac{2H(a)}{a^2} + \frac{v}{1 - v}m_\Theta(a)\right] + \frac{E\alpha}{1 - v}[n_\Theta(a) - \Theta(a, z)].$$

3. Determine m_r and m_θ at the clamped edge $r = a$ of a solid circular plate.

HINT: Substitute Equation (4.32) into Equations (4.29) to get

$$m_r = -2(1 + v)\alpha K\frac{H(a)}{a^2}, \qquad m_\theta = vm_r - (1 - v^2)\alpha Km_\Theta.$$

4. Show that $m_r = m_\theta$ at the center of a solid circular plate.

HINT: Use the rule of *De l'Hôspital* to determine $\lim_{r\to 0} H/r^2$ in Equations (4.29).

5. Determine the constants of integration $C_1, \ldots, C_4$ in Equation (4.27) for an annular plate clamped at its outer edge $r = a$ and free at its inner edge $r = b$.

HINT: Use boundary conditions $w = 0$, $dw/dr = 0$ at $r = a$, and $q_r = 0$, $m_r = 0$ at $r = b$ to obtain

$$C_1 = -C_2 a^2 = -\frac{1 - v}{2}\frac{H(a) - H(b)}{1 - v + (1 + v)b^2/a^2},$$

$$C_3 = H(a) + 2C_1, \qquad C_4 = 0.$$

6. Determine the constants of integration $C_1, \ldots, C_4$ in Equation (4.27) for an annular plate free at its outer edge $r = a$ and clamped at its inner edge $r = b$.

HINT: Proceed as in Problem 5, with boundary conditions interchanged, to obtain

$$C_1 = -\left(1 - 2\log\frac{b}{a}\right)C_2 b^2 - \int_b^a \frac{H(r)}{r}\,dr, \qquad C_2 = -\frac{1-\nu}{2b^2}\frac{H(a)}{1 - \nu + (1+\nu)a^2 b^2},$$
$$C_3 = -2C_2 b^2, \qquad C_4 = 0.$$

7. Use the influence function method to determine deflection $w(r)$ and bending moments $m_r(r)$, $m_\theta(r)$ due to a hot circular region $0 \leqslant r \leqslant R$ in an infinite circular plate. The temperature within the region has zero mean n_Θ and constant moment m_Θ, and is zero outside of the region. Show that the moment m_θ suffers a discontinuity across the line $r = R$.

HINT: In Equation (4.33), write $d\xi\,d\eta = r\,dr\,d\theta$ and use the relation

$$\frac{1}{2\pi}\int_0^{2\pi} d\theta \int_0^R r\log s\,dr = \begin{cases} \frac{1}{2}R^2\log r, & r \geqslant R, \\[2mm] \frac{1}{2}\left[R^2\left(\log R - \frac{1}{2}\right) + \frac{r^2}{2}\right], & r \leqslant R. \end{cases}$$

The discontinuity is $(1 - \nu^2)K\alpha m_\Theta$.

8. Solve Problem 7 for a circular plate of *finite* radius $a \geqslant R$, simply supported along $r = a$. Compare solution with Equation (4.31).

HINT: The solution of Problem 7 leaves a nonzero bending moment m_r and a nonzero deflection w along the edge $r = a$. Remove it by superposing the solution for an isothermal circular plate under the action of an edge moment $-m_r$.

9. Solve Problem 7 for a circular plate of finite radius $a \geqslant R$, clamped along $r = a$. Compare solution with Equation (4.32).

HINT: The solution of Problem 7 leaves a nonzero slope dw/dr along the edge $r = a$. Superpose suitable edge moments m_r to make the slope vanish.

10. Use the method described in Section 4.9 to solve the problem of a rectangular plate simply supported along all four edges and under the action of a uniform temperature moment $m_\Theta = M$.

HINT: Replace the last condition in (4.52) by $\partial^2 U/\partial y^2 = -M$ and change the last equation in (4.53) correspondingly. Solve for the $A_n, \ldots, D_n$ to obtain

$$A_n = -\frac{4M}{n\pi}, \qquad B_n = 0, \qquad C_n = \frac{4M}{n\pi}\frac{\cosh\alpha_n b - 1}{\sinh\alpha_n b}, \qquad D_n = 0 \qquad (n\text{ odd}),$$
$$A_n = B_n = C_n = D_n = 0 \qquad (n\text{ even}).$$

11. Use the method of Section 4.9 to solve the problem of a rectangular plate acted upon by a uniform temperature moment $m_\Theta = M$ if both edges $y = 0$ and $y = b$ are clamped.

HINT: The second boundary condition in (4.52) is now replaced by $\partial U/\partial y = 0$. Change the corresponding equation in (4.53) and solve for the $A_n, \ldots, D_n$.

12. Improve the eigenvalue λ in Section 4.11, for the case where $p_i = 0$ for $i \geqslant 3$, by adding one more term in the series representation for w. Compare the two results if $p_1 = -2$. Put $\mu = 1$.

HINT: The improved series will be

$$w = \sin \frac{s\pi x}{a} \left(A_1 \sin \frac{\pi y}{b} + A_3 \sin \frac{3\pi y}{b} \right).$$

Substitute to find the two equations

$$\left[\left(\mu + \frac{1}{\mu} \right)^2 \frac{1}{\lambda} - 1 \right] A_1 - \frac{8}{\pi} \left(\frac{1}{3} A_1 - \frac{1}{15} A_3 \right) p_1 = 0,$$

$$\left[\left(\mu + \frac{9}{\mu} \right)^2 \frac{1}{\lambda} - 1 \right] A_3 - \frac{8}{\pi} \left(-\frac{1}{15} A_1 + \frac{9}{35} A_3 \right) p_1 = 0.$$

The solution is $\lambda = -5.68$. The eigenvalue corresponding to the one-term expansion (4.63) is $\lambda = -5.75$.

The minus sign indicates that the temperature distribution would have to change sign in order to become critical.

13. For the plate discussed in Section 4.11, determine the reduction in the lowest natural frequency due to the membrane stress of Equation (4.62).

HINT: Use Equations (4.63) for W, together with Equation (4.55) to obtain $\rho h \omega^2$. Then determine $\rho h \omega_0^2$ for the unstressed plate by putting $n_x = 0$ in Equation (4.55):

$$\rho h \omega_0^2 = K \frac{\pi^4}{b^4} (1 + \mu^2)^2, \qquad \omega^2 = \omega_0^2 \left[1 - \frac{1}{\left(\mu + \frac{1}{\mu} \right)^2} \left(1 + \frac{8}{\pi} \sum_{k=1,3,5} \frac{p_k}{k(k^2 - 4)} \right) \right].$$

14. Determine the lowest eigenvalue λ for buckling of a solid circular plate simply supported along its edge $r = a$, and subject to the membrane force

$$n_r = -\frac{\pi^2 K}{a^2} \cos \frac{\pi r}{2a}.$$

HINT: The approximate solution

$$w = A \cos \frac{\pi r}{2a}$$

satisfies the kinematic boundary condition $w = 0$ at $r = a$, but not the dynamic condition $m_r = 0$. Hence, a fictitious edge moment

$$m = -K \left(\frac{d^2 w}{dr^2} + \frac{\nu}{r} \frac{dw}{dr} \right) = A K \nu \frac{\pi}{2a^2}$$

will appear in Equation (4.61). For $L[w]$, one has from Equation (4.23),

$$L[w] = K\nabla^2\nabla^2 w - \frac{\lambda}{r}\frac{d}{dr}\left(rn_r\frac{dw}{dr}\right).$$

The eigenvalue is

$$\lambda = \frac{9}{4(3\pi - 4)}\left[2v + \frac{\pi^2 - 4}{8} + C + \log\pi - Ci(\pi)\right] = 0.8295v + 0.9878,$$

where

$$Ci(\pi) = -\int_{\pi}^{\infty}\frac{\cos u}{u}\,du,$$

and C is the Eulerian constant.

CHAPTER 5

General Thermoelastic Theory

IN THE PRECEDING chapters, deformations (relative to the dimensions of the body) and temperature changes (relative to the initial absolute temperature) have been assumed to be small. The most important consequence of these assumptions was the linearity of the basic equations and, hence, the validity of the principle of superposition making the powerful methods of linear mathematics applicable.

There are, of course, limitations to this theory. First of all, neither deformations nor temperature changes are small in all circumstances. As an important example of large deformations, the postbuckling behavior of thin-walled structures may be mentioned. In order to be considered small, temperature changes would, in fact, have to be restricted to an interval of not more than 30 to 40°C. In reality, much larger changes occur quite frequently. Secondly, only the precise knowledge of the general equations of thermoelasticity enables us to establish bounds for the validity of the linearized procedure and estimate the errors involved in its application.

In the following, the basic equations of thermoelasticity will be set up in their general form.† Since we are dealing with nonisothermal processes this necessarily involves thermodynamic considerations.

5.1. Kinematic Relations

Let the position of a general point P of a body in its initial state‡ at time $t = 0$ be given by coordinates x_1, x_2, x_3 in a rectangular cartesian coordinate

---

† For a more detailed derivation of the results presented in Sections 5.1 and 5.2 the reader is referred to [2]. A theory of thermoelasticity from a very general point of view may be found in reference [21], Section 96.
‡ Since all deformations will be referred to this state, it will be called "undeformed."

system, fixed in space. Let e_1, e_2, e_3 be the corresponding system of base vectors (Figure 5.1). We then have†

$$d\mathbf{r} = \mathbf{e}_1\,dx_1 + \mathbf{e}_2\,dx_2 + \mathbf{e}_3\,dx_3 \equiv \mathbf{e}_i\,dx_i \tag{5.1}$$

for the line element in the undeformed body.

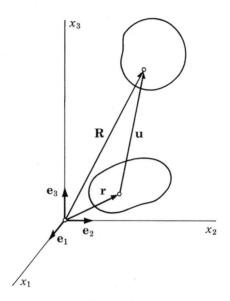

Figure 5.1

At time t, the body will have moved to a new position and the position vector of the point P will have changed from its initial value $\mathbf{r}$ to

$$\mathbf{R} = \mathbf{r} + \mathbf{u}, \tag{5.2}$$

where $\mathbf{u} = u_m\mathbf{e}_m$ represents the *displacement vector*. Analogous to Equation (5.1), we write

$$d\mathbf{R} = \mathbf{g}_i\,dx_i \tag{5.3}$$

for the line element in the deformed body. Base vectors $\mathbf{g}_i$ (Figure 5.2), form a nonorthogonal triad varying from point to point. This triad represents the deformed, originally orthogonal, triad of the base vectors $\mathbf{e}_i$.

---

† As is conventional in tensor analysis, the summation sign will be suppressed in this chapter. It is understood that, whenever an index appears twice in a term, this stands for the sum obtained by letting this index take on its values from 1 to 3.

In addition, the following notation will be used throughout this chapter,

$$\frac{\partial u_i}{\partial x_j} = u_{i,j}, \qquad \frac{\partial u_i}{\partial t} = \dot{u}_i, \text{ etc.}$$

The x_i are the initial coordinates of a point. We consider all quantities (displacement, temperature) associated with the point as functions of these coordinates† and of time t.‡ The coordinate surfaces x_i = const., which initially were orthogonal planes, deform into a system of nonorthogonal curved surfaces.

Differentiating Equation (5.2) with respect to x_i, we obtain

$$\mathbf{g}_i = \mathbf{e}_i + \mathbf{u}_{,i} = \mathbf{e}_i + u_{m,i}\mathbf{e}_m. \tag{5.4}$$

Using Equations (5.1), (5.3), and (5.4), we find for the squared line elements $(dr)^2$ and $(dR)^2$ in the undeformed and in the deformed body, respectively,

$$(dr)^2 = \delta_{ij}\, dx_i\, dx_j, \qquad (dR)^2 = g_{ij}\, dx_i\, dx_j, \tag{5.5}$$

where

$$\delta_{ij} = \mathbf{e}_i \cdot \mathbf{e}_j = \begin{cases} 1, & i = j \\ 0, & i \neq j \end{cases}, \qquad g_{ij} = \mathbf{g}_i \cdot \mathbf{g}_j = \delta_{ij} + 2e_{ij} \tag{5.6}$$

$$2e_{ij} = u_{i,j} + u_{j,i} + u_{m,i}u_{m,j}. \tag{5.7}$$

The nine quantities $e_{ij} = e_{ji}$ represent the components of the *Green strain tensor* defined as (half) the difference of the two *metric tensors* g_{ij} and δ_{ij} in the deformed and undeformed body, respectively.§

If displacement gradients $u_{m,i}$ are small compared with 1, the quadratic terms in Equation (5.7) may be neglected and Equation (5.7) reduces to the linear relation (2.10).

The term "metric tensor" refers to the fact that the nine quantities $g_{ij} = g_{ji}$ completely determine the metric, i.e., length and angles, in the deformed body. For instance, a line element ds_1 which was dx_1 in the direction of the base vector $\mathbf{e}_1$ in the undeformed body, has moved, after deformation, in the direction of the base vector $\mathbf{g}_1$, and its length has been stretched. From Equation (5.5), we see that with $dy = dz = 0$, its length is now

$$ds_1 = \sqrt{g_{11}}\, dx_1,$$

---

† In other words, the x_i are fixed on the point as an identification label throughout the entire deformation.

‡ In some instances, it is more convenient to use the instantaneous coordinates as independent variables. See references [2], [23], and [24].

§ As has been pointed out already on p. 6, a number of other definitions of strain are possible and in use. We mention the "right Cauchy-Green tensor" c_{ij} which, in the coordinate system used here, is identical with g_{ij}, and the "left Cauchy-Green tensor" defined by

$$b_{ij} = \delta_{ij} + u_{i,j} + u_{j,i} + u_{i,m}u_{j,m}.$$

There is, in general, no particular advantage of one choice over the other. The Green tensor selected here is probably the most widely used measure of strain in applied elasticity.

or, in general,†

$$ds_i = \sqrt{g_{(ii)}}\, dx_i.$$

Furthermore, the angle α_{ik} between the two directions $\mathbf{g}_i$ and $\mathbf{g}_k$ which, initially, was $\pi/2$, is given by

$$\cos \alpha_{ik} = \frac{\mathbf{g}_i \cdot \mathbf{g}_k}{|\mathbf{g}_i|\,|\mathbf{g}_k|} = \frac{g_{ik}}{\sqrt{g_{(ii)}g_{(kk)}}}. \tag{5.8}$$

Therefore, if the unit elongation $(ds_{(i)} - dx_{(i)})/dx_{(i)}$ of a fibre originally in the direction of x_i is denoted by ε_i, one has

$$1 + \varepsilon_i = \sqrt{g_{(ii)}} = \sqrt{1 + 2e_{(ii)}}. \tag{5.9}$$

Similarly, denoting the *decrease* in the right angle between the directions x_i and x_k by $\gamma_{ik} = \pi/2 - \alpha_{ik}$, it follows from Equations (5.6), (5.8), and (5.9) that

$$\sin \gamma_{ik} = \frac{2e_{(ik)}}{(1 + \varepsilon_i)(1 + \varepsilon_k)}. \tag{5.10}$$

5.2. Analysis of Stress

Consider a surface element dA whose normal was *initially* in the direction of $\mathbf{e}_1$ (Figure 5.2). The stress vector $\mathbf{s}_1$ acting on this element is then defined as the corresponding force divided by the *initial* area $dA_0 = dx_2\, dx_3$. Resolving $\mathbf{s}_1$ into three components in the direction of the three base vectors $\mathbf{g}_1, \mathbf{g}_2, \mathbf{g}_3$, one has

$$\mathbf{s}_1 = s_{11}\mathbf{g}_1 + s_{12}\mathbf{g}_2 + s_{13}\mathbf{g}_3.$$

In general, on a surface with normal initially in the direction of $\mathbf{e}_i$

$$\mathbf{s}_i = s_{ij}\mathbf{g}_j. \tag{5.11}$$

The nine quantities s_{ij} constitute the (second) *Piola-Kirchhoff stress tensor*.‡

If we denote by $\boldsymbol{\tau}_i$ the stress acting on a surface element with unit normal *after* deformation in the direction of $\mathbf{e}_i$, measured per unit area of the *deformed* surface, we write

$$\boldsymbol{\tau}_i = \tau_{ij}\mathbf{e}_j.$$

---

† Indices appearing in parentheses are not summed!
‡ See reference [21], Section 43A.

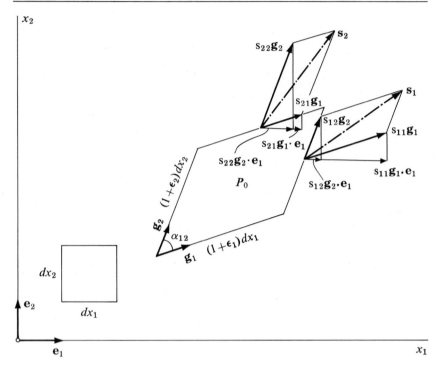

Figure 5.2

The stress tensor τ_{ij} is symmetric and is related to s_{ij} by[†]

$$\sqrt{g}\tau_{ij} = (u_{i,k} + \delta_{ik})(u_{j,l} + \delta_{jl})s_{kl},$$

where g is defined by Equation (5.18).

From the fact that the $\mathbf{g}_i$ are not unit vectors, we conclude immediately that the quantities s_{ij} are not stress components in a physical sense. Indeed, by using unit vectors $\mathbf{g}_i/\sqrt{g_{(ii)}}$, we may write Equation (5.11) in the form

$$\mathbf{s}_i = \sigma_{ij}\frac{\mathbf{g}_j}{\sqrt{g_{(jj)}}}, \qquad \sigma_{ij} = s_{ij}\sqrt{g_{(jj)}} = s_{ij}\sqrt{1 + 2e_{(jj)}}, \qquad (5.12)$$

where the σ_{ij} now represent physical (or engineering) stress components per unit area of the undeformed body. However, these components do not constitute a tensor, in contrast to the s_{ij}.

It is now a simple matter to formulate the equations of motion for an

---

† See reference [21], Section 43A.

element of the body with initial volume $dV_0 = dx_1\,dx_2\,dx_3$ and mass $dm = \rho_0\,dV_0 = \rho\,dV$ where ρ_0 is mass density in the undeformed state. Taking components in the x_1-direction of all force vectors $s_{11}\mathbf{g}_1\,dx_2\,dx_3$, etc., acting on the element (see Figure 5.2), multiplying with unit vector $\mathbf{e}_1$, and remembering that the stress vector $-s_{1j}\mathbf{g}_j$ on the left-hand surface of the element changes to $s_{1j}\mathbf{g}_j + (s_{1j}\mathbf{g}_j)_{,1}\,dx_1 + \cdots$ on the right-hand surface, with similar relations for the other surfaces, one finds from Cauchy's law,

$$[(s_{1j}\mathbf{g}_j)_{,1} + (s_{2j}\mathbf{g}_j)_{,2} + (s_{3j}\mathbf{g}_j)_{,3}]\cdot\mathbf{e}_1 + \rho_0 F_1 = \rho_0\ddot{u}_1,$$

where F_1 is the component in the x_1-direction of the external force vector $\mathbf{F}$ per unit mass. Two analogous relations are obtained for the x_2- and x_3-direction. From Equation (5.4), one has

$$\mathbf{g}_j\cdot\mathbf{e}_k = \mathbf{e}_j\cdot\mathbf{e}_k + u_{m,j}\mathbf{e}_m\cdot\mathbf{e}_k = \delta_{kj} + u_{k,j}. \tag{5.13}$$

Hence, the three equations of motion read

$$[s_{ij}(\delta_{kj} + u_{k,j})]_{,i} + \rho_0 F_k = \rho_0\ddot{u}_k. \tag{5.14}$$

Explicitly:

$$\frac{\partial}{\partial x_1}\left[s_{11}\left(1 + \frac{\partial u_1}{\partial x_1}\right) + s_{12}\frac{\partial u_1}{\partial x_2} + s_{13}\frac{\partial u_1}{\partial x_3}\right]$$

$$+\frac{\partial}{\partial x_2}\left[s_{21}\left(1 + \frac{\partial u_1}{\partial x_1}\right) + s_{22}\frac{\partial u_1}{\partial x_2} + s_{23}\frac{\partial u_1}{\partial x_3}\right]$$

$$+\frac{\partial}{\partial x_3}\left[s_{31}\left(1 + \frac{\partial u_1}{\partial x_1}\right) + s_{32}\frac{\partial u_1}{\partial x_2} + s_{33}\frac{\partial u_1}{\partial x_3}\right] + \rho_0 F_1 = \rho_0\frac{\partial^2 u_1}{\partial t^2},$$

$$\frac{\partial}{\partial x_1}\left[s_{11}\frac{\partial u_2}{\partial x_1} + s_{12}\left(1 + \frac{\partial u_2}{\partial x_2}\right) + s_{13}\frac{\partial u_2}{\partial x_3}\right]$$

$$+\frac{\partial}{\partial x_2}\left[s_{21}\frac{\partial u_2}{\partial x_1} + s_{22}\left(1 + \frac{\partial u_2}{\partial x_2}\right) + s_{23}\frac{\partial u_2}{\partial x_3}\right] \qquad (5.14a)$$

$$+\frac{\partial}{\partial x_3}\left[s_{31}\frac{\partial u_2}{\partial x_1} + s_{32}\left(1 + \frac{\partial u_2}{\partial x_2}\right) + s_{33}\frac{\partial u_2}{\partial x_3}\right] + \rho_0 F_2 = \rho_0\frac{\partial^2 u_2}{\partial t^2},$$

$$\frac{\partial}{\partial x_1}\left[s_{11}\frac{\partial u_3}{\partial x_1} + s_{12}\frac{\partial u_3}{\partial x_2} + s_{13}\left(1 + \frac{\partial u_3}{\partial x_3}\right)\right]$$

$$+\frac{\partial}{\partial x_2}\left[s_{21}\frac{\partial u_3}{\partial x_1} + s_{22}\frac{\partial u_3}{\partial x_2} + s_{23}\left(1 + \frac{\partial u_3}{\partial x_3}\right)\right]$$

$$+\frac{\partial}{\partial x_3}\left[s_{31}\frac{\partial u_3}{\partial x_1} + s_{32}\frac{\partial u_3}{\partial x_2} + s_{33}\left(1 + \frac{\partial u_3}{\partial x_3}\right)\right] + \rho_0 F_3 = \rho_0\frac{\partial^2 u_3}{\partial t^2}.$$

By taking moments of the force couples $s_{12}\mathbf{g}_2\,dx_2\,dx_3$ and $s_{21}\mathbf{g}_1\,dx_1\,dx_3$, acting on the element of Figure 5.2,

$$s_{12}\mathbf{g}_2\,dx_2\,dx_3 \times \mathbf{g}_1\,dx_1 + s_{21}\mathbf{g}_1\,dx_1\,dx_3 \times \mathbf{g}_2\,dx_2$$

$$= (s_{12} - s_{21})\mathbf{g}_2 \times \mathbf{g}_1\,dx_1\,dx_2\,dx_3,$$

and one obtains, for a body in equilibrium,

$$s_{12} = s_{21}$$

and, generally,

$$s_{ij} = s_{ji}. \tag{5.15}$$

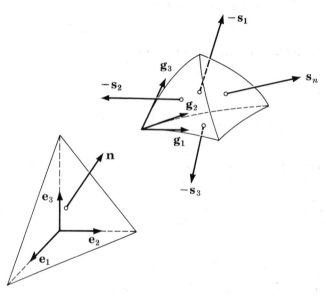

Figure 5.3

We assume that this *symmetry of the stress tensor* holds also for a moving body.

In order to conclude this brief analysis of stress, we consider a tetrahedron which originally had three of its edges in the directions $\mathbf{e}_1$, $\mathbf{e}_2$, $\mathbf{e}_3$ (Figure 5.3). Let $\mathbf{s}_n$ be the stress vector on the surface dA which, before deformation, had the normal vector $\mathbf{n}$. Then, $n_1\,dA$, $n_2\,dA$, and $n_3\,dA$ are the areas of the other three surfaces. Remembering that all stresses are referred to the undeformed areas, we write Cauchy's law of motion for the element

$$-\mathbf{s}_1 n_1\,dA - \mathbf{s}_2 n_2\,dA - \mathbf{s}_3 n_3\,dA + \mathbf{s}_n\,dA + \rho_0\mathbf{F}\,dV = \rho_0\ddot{\mathbf{u}}\,dV.$$

Dividing by dA and letting the volume dV shrink to zero, we get

$$\mathbf{s}_n = n_i \mathbf{s}_i. \tag{5.16}$$

We note that the state of stress $\mathbf{s}_n$ in a body is completely determined by the nine stress components.

5.3. Basic Equations

Three fundamental equations constitute the basis of the theory of thermo-elasticity. The first is the *law of motion*, as expressed in Equation (5.14). The second is the *law of conservation of mass*, which expresses the fact that the total mass of the body remains constant, that is,

$$\int_V \rho \, dV = \int_{V_0} \rho_0 \, dV_0, \tag{5.17}$$

where ρ is mass density. Due to deformation, the element of volume changes from its initial value $dV_0 = dx_1 \, dx_2 \, dx_3$ to

$$dV = d\mathbf{s}_1 \cdot (d\mathbf{s}_2 \times d\mathbf{s}_3) = \mathbf{g}_1 \cdot (\mathbf{g}_2 \times \mathbf{g}_3) \, dx_1 \, dx_2 \, dx_3 = \sqrt{g} \, dV_0,$$

where

$$g = \det |g_{ij}| = \det |\delta_{ij} + 2e_{ij}|. \tag{5.18}$$

Substituting into Equation (5.17), one finds

$$\rho = \frac{\rho_0}{\sqrt{g}}. \tag{5.19}$$

The third fundamental equation is the *law of conservation of energy*, or first law of thermodynamics

$$\frac{d}{dt} \int_m \tfrac{1}{2} \dot{u}_i \dot{u}_i \, dm + \frac{d}{dt} \int_m U \, dm = \int_m F_i \dot{u}_i \, dm + \oint_A f_i \dot{u}_i \, dA$$

$$+ \int_m R \, dm - \oint_A Q_i n_i \, dA. \tag{5.20}$$

Here, U denotes internal energy per unit mass, F_i is the body-force vector per unit mass, and f_i the applied surface stress. We let R equal the heat produced per unit time and unit mass by heat sources distributed within the body, and Q_i be the heat-flux through the surface of the body, positive outwards, while n_i denotes the surface unit normal vector, directed outwards. Both f_i and Q_i are referred to the unit area of the deformed body.

The first and second term on the left-hand side of Equation (5.20) represent the rate of change of kinetic energy and internal energy, respectively. They are equal to the rate of work done by all external forces, and to the amount of heat produced per unit time within the body plus the heat transported into the body from the outside.

Equation (5.20) may be transformed into a more convenient form with the aid of the *principle of rate of work*. This principle states that the rate of change of kinetic energy equals the rate of work of all forces, external and internal. Per unit of initial volume, the latter equals† $-\mathbf{s}_i \cdot \dot{\mathbf{u}}_{,i}$ or, using $\dot{\mathbf{u}} = \dot{u}_k \mathbf{e}_k$ and Equations (5.11), (5.13), and (5.7),

$$-\mathbf{s}_i \cdot \dot{\mathbf{u}}_{,i} = -s_{ij}\dot{u}_{k,i}\mathbf{g}_j \cdot \mathbf{e}_k = -s_{ij}\dot{u}_{k,i}(\delta_{kj} + u_{k,j}) = -s_{ij}\dot{e}_{ij}.$$

The principle of rate of work thus reads

$$\frac{d}{dt}\int_m \tfrac{1}{2}\dot{u}_i\dot{u}_i \, dm = \int_m F_i\dot{u}_i \, dm + \oint_A f_i\dot{u}_i \, dA - \int_{V_0} s_{ij}\dot{e}_{ij} \, dV_0.$$

Substitution into Equation (5.20) gives

$$\int_m (\dot{U} - R) \, dm = \int_{V_0} s_{ij}\dot{e}_{ij} \, dV_0 - \oint_A Q_i n_i \, dA.$$

Putting $dm = \rho_0 \, dV_0$ and applying Gauss' theorem (**a** being an arbitrary vector),

$$\oint_A a_i n_i \, dA = \int_A \frac{1}{\sqrt{g}}(a_i\sqrt{g})_{,i} \, dV,$$

with $dV = \sqrt{g} \, dV_0$ to the surface integral, one obtains, finally,

$$\rho_0(\dot{U} - R) = s_{ij}\dot{e}_{ij} - q_{i,i}. \tag{5.21}$$

Here, $q_i = Q_i\sqrt{g}$ represents the heat-flux vector within the body, referred to the unit area of the undeformed body.

Now, the *second law of thermodynamics*, in the form of the Clausius–Duhem inequality,‡ states that

$$\frac{d}{dt}\int_m S \, dm \geqslant \int_m \frac{R}{T} \, dm - \oint_A \frac{Q_i n_i}{T} \, dA,$$

where T is absolute temperature and S is entropy per unit mass. Using Gauss' theorem, one is led to

$$\rho_0 T \dot{S} \geqslant \rho_0 R - q_{i,i} + \frac{q_i}{T} T_{,i} \tag{5.22}$$

or, upon elimination of R between Equations (5.21) and (5.22)

$$\rho_0(\dot{U} - T\dot{S}) \leqslant s_{ij}\dot{e}_{ij} - \frac{q_i}{T} T_{,i}. \tag{5.23}$$

---

† Since the work is absorbed in the body, a minus sign has to be affixed.
‡ See reference [21], p. 364.

We now introduce the so-called *Helmholtz free energy* Φ defined by

$$\Phi = U - TS. \tag{5.24}$$

For an elastic material Φ and S depend only on the quantities e_{ij} and T, while the heat-flux vector q_i will, in general, depend on e_{ij}, T, and the temperature gradient $T_{,i}$. Then

$$\dot{\Phi} = \frac{\partial \Phi}{\partial e_{ij}} \dot{e}_{ij} + \frac{\partial \Phi}{\partial T} \dot{T}.$$

Substituting this into Equations (5.21) and (5.23), we have

$$\left(\rho_0 \frac{\partial \Phi}{\partial e_{ij}} - s_{ij} \right) \dot{e}_{ij} + \rho_0 \left(\frac{\partial \Phi}{\partial T} + S \right) \dot{T} + \rho_0 (T\dot{S} - R) + q_{i,i} = 0,$$

$$\left(\rho_0 \frac{\partial \Phi}{\partial e_{ij}} - s_{ij} \right) \dot{e}_{ij} + \rho_0 \left(\frac{\partial \Phi}{\partial T} + S \right) \dot{T} + \frac{q_i}{T} T_{,i} \leqslant 0.$$

Since $\dot{e}_{ij}$ and $\dot{T}$ are arbitrary, and q_i and the expressions within the parentheses in the inequality do not depend on these quantities, we conclude that

$$s_{ij} = \rho_0 \frac{\partial \Phi}{\partial e_{ij}}, \tag{5.25}$$

$$S = -\frac{\partial \Phi}{\partial T}, \tag{5.26}$$

$$q_{i,i} = \rho_0 (R - T\dot{S}), \tag{5.27}$$

and

$$q_i T_{,i} \leqslant 0.$$

Equations (5.25) and (5.26) are *constitutive equations* of the material. Equation (5.25) represents the stress-strain law, while Equation (5.26) defines entropy. Substitution of Equation (5.26) into Equation (5.27) leads to the equation of *heat conduction*

$$q_{i,i} = \rho_0 T \left(\frac{\partial^2 \Phi}{\partial e_{ij} \partial T} \dot{e}_{ij} + \frac{\partial^2 \Phi}{\partial T^2} \dot{T} \right) + \rho_0 R. \tag{5.28}$$

We note the coupling present between temperature T and strain e_{ij}.

The sixteen scalar relations of Equations (5.7), (5.14), (5.25), and (5.28) form the basic equations of thermoelasticity. They contain u_i, e_{ij}, s_{ij}, and T as sixteen unknown functions of space x_i and time t. Associated with these equations are initial and boundary conditions as discussed in Chapter 2.

5.4. The Elastic Potential

The stress-strain relations of Equation (5.25) may also be written in the form

$$s_{ij} = \frac{\partial W}{\partial e_{ij}}, \tag{5.29}$$

where $W = \rho_0 \Phi$ is the *elastic potential* per unit volume of the unstrained body.

In an *isotropic* solid, W cannot depend on the individual e_{ij}, but only on three independent invariants I_1, I_2, I_3 of the strain tensor, and on the temperature T:

$$W = W(I_1, I_2, I_3, T). \tag{5.30}$$

Equation (5.29) then goes over into

$$s_{ij} = \frac{\partial W}{\partial I_1} \frac{\partial I_1}{\partial e_{ij}} + \frac{\partial W}{\partial I_2} \frac{\partial I_2}{\partial e_{ij}} + \frac{\partial W}{\partial I_3} \frac{\partial I_3}{\partial e_{ij}}.$$

The invariants may be taken to be†

$$I_1 = e_{ii}, \qquad I_2 = \tfrac{1}{2} e_{ij} e_{ij}, \qquad I_3 = \tfrac{1}{3} e_{ik} e_{il} e_{kl}. \tag{5.31}$$

Then,

$$s_{ij} = \frac{\partial W}{\partial I_1} \delta_{ij} + \frac{\partial W}{\partial I_2} e_{ij} + \frac{\partial W}{\partial I_3} e_{ik} e_{jk}. \tag{5.32}$$

For convenience in computational work, we list the explicit expressions,

$$\left.\begin{aligned}
I_1 &= e_{11} + e_{22} + e_{33}, \\
2I_2 &= e_{11}^2 + e_{22}^2 + e_{33}^2 + 2(e_{12}^2 + e_{23}^2 + e_{31}^2), \\
3I_3 &= e_{11}^3 + e_{22}^3 + e_{33}^3 + 3[e_{12}^2(e_{11} + e_{22}) + e_{23}^2(e_{22} + e_{33}) \\
&\qquad\qquad + e_{31}^2(e_{33} + e_{11})] + 6e_{12}e_{23}e_{31}.
\end{aligned}\right\} \tag{5.31a}$$

Other choices of invariants are, of course, possible.‡

A frequently used class of stress-strain relations is obtained by writing W as a *polynomial* in I_1, I_2, I_3, and T. The existence of a *reference state* of the solid at a uniform temperature T_0 is assumed for which the body is free of stress. Displacements and strain will be referred to this state, and the reference value of W will be taken as zero. No constant terms can then be present in W. We therefore write,

$$W = \sum_{i=1}^{4} a_i I_i + \sum_{i=1}^{4} \sum_{j=1}^{4} [A_{ij} I_i I_j + B_{ij} I_i I_j^2 + \cdots], \tag{5.33}$$

---

† See reference [22].
‡ See reference [1], p. 19 and reference [2], §2.8.

where

$$I_4 = T - T_0 = \Theta.$$ (5.34)

Differentiation of Equation (5.33) yields

$$\frac{\partial W}{\partial I_k} = a_k + \sum_{i=1}^{4} [(A_{ik} + A_{ki})I_i + (2B_{ik}I_iI_k + B_{ki}I_i^2) + \cdots]$$

$$(k \text{ not summed!}). \quad (5.35)$$

Since $e_{ij} = 0$ and, hence, $I_1 = I_2 = I_3 = I_4 = 0$ in the reference state, it follows from Equation (5.32) that

$$a_1 = 0.$$ (5.36)

Putting, in addition, $a_4 = 0$ makes the entropy $S = 0$ in the reference state.

In a *homogeneous solid* the coefficients a_i, A_{ij}, B_{ij}, ... will be independent of the coordinates x_i.

The choice of the elastic potential W also specifies the equation of heat conduction [see Equation (5.28)], which may be written in the form

$$q_{i,i} = T\left(\frac{\partial s_{ij}}{\partial \Theta}\dot{e}_{ij} + \frac{\partial^2 W}{\partial \Theta^2}\dot{\Theta}\right) + \rho_0 R.$$ (5.37)

As has been mentioned above, the heat-flux vector q_i in the most general case will be a function of the scalar T, the vector $T_{,i}$, and the symmetric tensor e_{ij}. It has been shown† that in the *isotropic* case such a function must necessarily have the form

$$q_i = (\varphi_0\delta_{ij} + \varphi_1 e_{ij} + \varphi_2 e_{ik}e_{kj})T_{,j},$$ (5.38)

where the φ_k are scalar functions of the following seven invariants, which, in contradistinction to Equation (5.30), depend on the temperature gradient:

$$I_1; I_2; I_3; T; T_{,i}; \quad e_{ij}T_{,i}T_{,j}; \quad e_{ik}e_{kj}T_{,i}T_{,j}.$$ (5.39)

In particular, the φ_k may be taken as polynomials in these invariants.

5.5. Inversion of the Stress-Strain Law

We introduce the Legendre transform

$$W^*(s_{ij}, T) = e_{ij}s_{ij} - W(e_{ij}, T)$$ (5.40)

of the elastic potential W. Taking differentials, we have

$$\frac{\partial W^*}{\partial s_{ij}}ds_{ij} + \frac{\partial W^*}{\partial T}dT = e_{ij}\,ds_{ij} + s_{ij}\,de_{ij} - \frac{\partial W}{\partial e_{ij}}de_{ij} - \frac{\partial W}{\partial T}\,dT.$$

---

† See reference [21], p. 35.

Comparison of coefficients reproduces Equation (5.29), together with

$$e_{ij} = \frac{\partial W^*}{\partial s_{ij}}, \qquad \frac{\partial W^*}{\partial T} = -\frac{\partial W}{\partial T}. \qquad (5.41)$$

The function $-W^*$ is known as the *Gibbs' function* per unit volume of the unstrained body.

The first of Equations (5.41) represents the inversion of the stress-strain law of Equation (5.29).

For an *isotropic solid*, W^* will be a function of the three invariants J_1, J_2, J_3 of the stress tensor, and of temperature T:

$$W^* = W^*(J_1, J_2, J_3, T). \qquad (5.42)$$

If we choose, in analogy to Equation (5.31),

$$J_1 = s_{ii}, \qquad J_2 = \tfrac{1}{2}s_{ij}s_{ij}, \qquad J_3 = \tfrac{1}{3}s_{ik}s_{il}s_{kl}, \qquad (5.43)$$

then the strain-stress law reads

$$e_{ij} = \frac{\partial W^*}{\partial J_1}\delta_{ij} + \frac{\partial W^*}{\partial J_2}s_{ij} + \frac{\partial W^*}{\partial J_3}s_{ik}s_{jk}. \qquad (5.44)$$

The actual inversion of a given stress-strain law is, in general, a tedious procedure. One first determines W^* from Equation (5.40) in terms of e_{ij} and T using Equation (5.32):

$$W^* = I_1\frac{\partial W}{\partial I_1} + 2I_2\frac{\partial W}{\partial I_2} + 3I_3\frac{\partial W}{\partial I_3} - W. \qquad (5.45)$$

Now, W^* on the left-hand side of this equation is written as a polynomial in J_1, J_2, J_3 and $\Theta = T - T_0$, with unknown coefficients. These coefficients follow by expressing the J_i in terms of the I_i by means of Equation (5.32), and by comparing coefficients in the resulting power series.

5.6. Some Simple Cases

Stress without deformation

With $e_{ij} = 0$, we have from Equation (5.32)

$$s_{ij} = \frac{\partial W}{\partial I_1}\delta_{ij} = p\delta_{ij}. \qquad (5.46)$$

A uniform tension p or hydrostatic pressure $-p$ will, therefore, be present in an isotropic body counteracting the change of volume due to a uniform temperature change Θ. If the elastic potential W is of the polynomial form of Equation (5.33), we find, from Equation (5.35), using $I_1 = I_2 = I_3 = 0$, that

$$p = \frac{\partial W}{\partial I_1} = (A_{14} + A_{41})\Theta + B_{14}\Theta^2. \tag{5.47}$$

All other terms drop out.

Deformation without stress

Putting $s_{ij} = 0$ in Equation (5.44), we obtain

$$e_{ij} = \frac{\partial W^*}{\partial J_1} \delta_{ij} = \varepsilon\delta_{ij}.$$

The isotropic body will be in a state of uniform dilation, i.e., there will be a change of its volume but not of its shape. From Equation (5.6) there follows

$$g_{ij} = (1 + 2\varepsilon)\delta_{ij},$$

and from Equation (5.18),

$$\frac{dV - dV_0}{dV_0} = \sqrt{g} - 1 = (1 + 2\varepsilon)^{3/2} - 1. \tag{5.48}$$

For small ε, this reduces to 3ε.

The relation for ε corresponding to Equation (5.47) is quite obvious.

Elastic potential does not depend on I_3

Equation (5.32) reduces to

$$s_{ij} = \frac{\partial W}{\partial I_1} \delta_{ij} + \frac{\partial W}{\partial I_2} e_{ij}. \tag{5.49}$$

The inverse law, Equation (5.44), is then necessarily of the form

$$e_{ij} = \frac{\partial W^*}{\partial J_1} \delta_{ij} + \frac{\partial W^*}{\partial J_2} s_{ij}. \tag{5.50}$$

For a proof, one first notes that W^* in Equation (5.45) depends on I_1, I_2, and Θ only. Therefore, it cannot depend on J_3 since J_3, in turn, depends on I_3.

Linear law

It follows from Equation (5.32) that for a linear stress-strain relation W must be independent of I_3, linear in I_2, and quadratic in I_1:

$$W = a_2 I_2 + A_{11} I_1^2 + A_{14} I_1 \Theta + A_{44}\Theta^2 + B_{44}\Theta^3 + \cdots.$$

In the usual notation [see Equation (2.9)], one writes

$$W = G\left(2I_2 + \frac{\nu}{1-2\nu} I_1^2 - \frac{2(1+\nu)}{1-2\nu} \alpha I_1 \Theta\right) + f(\Theta). \qquad (5.51)$$

The corresponding stress-strain law (*Hooke's law*) is

$$s_{ij} = 2G\left(e_{ij} + \frac{\nu}{1-2\nu} e_{kk}\delta_{ij} - \frac{1+\nu}{1-2\nu} \alpha\Theta\delta_{ij}\right).$$

The equation of heat conduction, Equation (5.37), is basically nonlinear. However, if the temperature deviation Θ from the reference temperature T_0 is small, the factor T in Equation (5.37) may be replaced by T_0. Omitting, in addition, terms of order higher than Θ^2 in Equation (5.51), and adopting as constitutive equation the linear Fourier law (2.11) by putting $\varphi_0 = -k$, $\varphi_1 = \varphi_2 = 0$ in Equation (5.38),

$$q_i = -k\Theta_{,i}, \qquad (5.52)$$

one is led to the linear relation

$$k\nabla^2\Theta = 2\frac{1+\nu}{1-2\nu} G\alpha T_0\dot{e}_{ii} - 2T_0 A_{44}\dot{\Theta} - \rho_0 R. \qquad (5.53)$$

Comparison with Equation (2.12), with $\rho_0 R \equiv S$, gives

$$A_{44} = -\frac{c\rho_0}{2T_0}.$$

The "coupling term"

$$\frac{2(1+\nu)}{1-2\nu} G\alpha T_0\dot{e}_{ii}$$

appears as an additional source of heat which has been neglected in Equation (2.12). If $\dot{e}_{ii}$ is negative (compression), there will be heating of the body as a result of deformation, while during extension, where $\dot{e}_{ii}$ is positive, there will be cooling (*Gough-Joule effect*).

The elastic potential for the linear *anisotropic body* is given by

$$W = \frac{a}{2T_0}\Theta^2 + b_{ij}e_{ij}\Theta + \tfrac{1}{2}c_{ijkl}e_{ij}e_{kl}, \qquad (5.54)$$

with the corresponding stress-strain relation

$$s_{ij} = b_{ij}\Theta + c_{ijkl}e_{kl}, \qquad (5.55)$$

while the equation of heat conduction has the form

$$q_i = -a_{ij}\Theta_{,j}. \qquad (5.56)$$

Thus, from Equation (5.37),

$$-(a_{ij}\Theta_{,j})_{,i} = a\dot{\Theta} + T_0 b_{ij}\dot{e}_{ij} + \rho_0 R. \qquad (5.57)$$

Taking into account the symmetry of the stress and strain tensors in Equation (5.55), and the symmetry of a_{ij} (the "Onsager relation"), and noting from Equation (5.54) that $c_{ijkl} = c_{klij}$, one finds that in the general anisotropic case there are altogether thirty-three independent coefficients: six b_{ij}, twenty-one c_{ijkl}, and six a_{ij}. The number is reduced if the body exhibits certain properties of elastic and thermal symmetry.

5.7. Isotropic Incompressible Material

We call a material incompressible if its volume does not change under the action of any stress or temperature (isochoric response).† From Equation (5.18), we note that $g = 1$ for such a material. Taking this constraint into account by means of a Lagrangian multiplier, we may replace the elastic potential W by $W - \dfrac{p}{2}(g - 1)$ in Equation (5.29). From Equation (5.18), we find

$$\frac{\partial g}{\partial e_{ij}} = 2G_{ij}, \qquad (5.58)$$

where G_{ij} is the cofactor of g_{ij}, obtained by erasing in $\det|g_{ij}|$ the ith row and the jth column and multiplying by $(-1)^{i+j}$. Thus, Equation (5.32) is to be replaced by

$$s_{ij} = \frac{\partial W}{\partial I_1}\delta_{ij} + \frac{\partial W}{\partial I_2}e_{ij} + \frac{\partial W}{\partial I_3}e_{ik}e_{jk} - pG_{ij}. \qquad (5.59)$$

The Lagrangian multiplier $-p$ represents a hydrostatic pressure and the stress in the body is determined from the deformation only to within this pressure.

Neither hydrostatic pressure nor uniform temperature produces any change in shape or volume of an incompressible isotropic body, i.e., all e_{ij} remain unchanged in this case. It follows from Equation (5.44) that $\partial W^*/\partial J_i$ cannot depend on T. From the second of Equations (5.41), we conclude then that $\partial W/\partial I_i$ must also be independent of T: "In an incompressible isotropic body, stress and strain are independent of temperature." Equation (5.37) for the heat flow reduces to

$$q_{i,i} = T\dot{\Theta}\frac{\partial^2 W}{\partial\Theta^2} + \rho_0 R. \qquad (5.60)$$

---

† If this is true for the stress, but not for the temperature, the body is called "mechanically incompressible."

5.8. Example: Torsion of an Incompressible Cylinder†

Let an isotropic incompressible circular cylinder be twisted by rotating its cross sections through an angle $\chi = cz$ about the axis z. We have then, with θ as polar angle,

$$x + u = r \cos (\theta + \chi), \qquad y + v = r \sin (\theta + \chi), \qquad w = 0,$$

or

$$u = x \cos \chi - y \sin \chi - x$$
$$v = x \sin \chi + y \cos \chi - y$$
$$w = 0.$$

Substituting into Equations (5.7), one obtains for the components of strain

$$e_{xx} = e_{yy} = e_{xy} = 0, \qquad 2e_{xz} = -cy, \qquad 2e_{yz} = cx, \qquad 2e_{zz} = c^2 r^2.$$

Putting this into $g = \det |\delta_{ij} + 2e_{ij}|$, we find $g = 1$. The deformation is, therefore, isochoric, as assumed above.

Now, let the cylinder be heated to a *temperature gradient* uniform along the axis:· $\Theta = kz$. Since the body is incompressible, this introduces no additional deformation. We wish to find the heat flow in the body.

It is convenient to transform Equation (5.38) to cylindrical coordinates. The law of tensor transformation gives

$$e'_{ij} = a_{il} a_{jm} e_{lm}, \tag{5.61}$$

where the a_{il} are directional cosines and, for cylindrical coordinates, are given by

$$a_{rx} = \cos \theta, \qquad a_{ry} = \sin \theta, \qquad a_{\theta x} = -\sin \theta, \qquad a_{\theta y} = \cos \theta,$$

$$a_{rz} = a_{\theta z} = a_{zx} = a_{zy} = 0, \qquad a_{zz} = 1.$$

After substitution,

$$\left. \begin{aligned}
e_{rr} &= e_{xx} \cos^2 \theta + e_{xy} \sin 2\theta + e_{yy} \sin^2 \theta, \\
e_{\theta\theta} &= e_{xx} \sin^2 \theta - e_{xy} \sin 2\theta + e_{yy} \cos^2 \theta, \\
e_{r\theta} &= e_{xy} \cos 2\theta + \tfrac{1}{2}(e_{yy} - e_{xx}) \sin 2\theta, \\
e_{rz} &= e_{xz} \cos \theta + e_{yz} \sin \theta, \\
e_{\theta z} &= -e_{xz} \sin \theta + e_{yz} \cos \theta.
\end{aligned} \right\} \tag{5.62}$$

It follows in the present case that

$$e_{rr} = e_{\theta\theta} = e_{r\theta} = e_{rz} = 0, \qquad e_{\theta z} = \tfrac{1}{2} cr, \qquad e_{zz} = \tfrac{1}{2} c^2 r^2.$$

† See reference [21], p. 359.

Equation (5.38) now reads

$$q_i = \varphi_0 T_{,i} + \varphi_1 e_{ij} T_{,j} + \varphi_2 e_{ik} e_{kj} T_{,j},$$

where $i, j, k = r, \theta, z$, and $T_{,\theta}$ is to be interpreted as $1/r(\partial T/\partial \theta)$. Substituting the values from above, one gets

$$q_r = 0,$$

$$q_\theta = \frac{k}{4} cr(\varphi_1 + c^2 r^2 \varphi_2),$$

$$q_z = \frac{k}{4} [4\varphi_0 + 2c^2 r^2 \varphi_1 + (1 + c^2 r^2) c^2 r^2 \varphi_2].$$

We observe that, unless $\varphi_1 = \varphi_2 = 0$, heat flows not only in the direction of the temperature gradient, but also perpendicular to it in the circumferential direction. This is, of course, due to the anisotropy that has developed in the originally isotropic body as a consequence of deformation. The lines of heat flow are helices in the cylindrical surfaces $r = $ const., with pitch equal to q_θ/rq_z.

Since $q_r = 0$, the solution is valid provided the lateral surface of the cylinder is insulated.

All strain components are independent of z and, therefore, so are the stresses. The cylinder retains its diameter and length while generating lines are twisted into helices with angle $\gamma_{z\theta}$. From Equations (5.10) and (5.9) we find $\tan \gamma_{z\theta} = cr$. The stress components on a surface $r = $ const. are, from Equation (5.59)

$$\left.\begin{aligned}
s_{r\theta} &= \frac{\partial W}{\partial I_2} e_{r\theta} + \frac{\partial W}{\partial I_3} [e_{r\theta}(e_{rr} + e_{\theta\theta}) + e_{rz}e_{\theta z}] - pG_{r\theta}, \\
s_{rz} &= \frac{\partial W}{\partial I_2} e_{rz} + \frac{\partial W}{\partial I_3} [e_{rz}(e_{rr} + e_{zz}) + e_{r\theta}e_{\theta z}] - pG_{rz}, \\
s_{rr} &= \frac{\partial W}{\partial I_1} + \frac{\partial W}{\partial I_2} e_{rr} + \frac{\partial W}{\partial I_3} (e_{rr}^2 + e_{r\theta}^2 + e_{rz}^2) - pG_{rr}.
\end{aligned}\right\} \quad (5.63)$$

Utilizing Equations (5.61) with e_{ij} replaced by G_{ij}, together with

$$G_{xx} = 1 + c^2 y^2, \qquad G_{xy} = -c^2 xy, \qquad G_{yy} = 1 + c^2 x^2,$$

$$G_{xz} = cy, \qquad G_{yz} = -cx,$$

one finds

$$G_{rr} = 1, \qquad G_{r\theta} = G_{rz} = 0.$$

Substitution of these values and of the strain components into Equations (5.63) yields

$$s_{r\theta} = s_{rz} = 0, \qquad s_{rr} = \frac{\partial W}{\partial I_1} - p,$$

where s_{rr} and $s_{r\theta}$ are normal stress in the radial direction and shearing stress in the circumferential direction,† respectively, and s_{rz} is the shearing stress in the direction of the twisted generating lines. The lateral surface $r = R$ of the cylinder is, therefore, free of shearing stresses. The normal stress may also be removed by superposing a properly chosen uniform pressure p. Thus, in order to maintain the rod in equilibrium, external forces (equipollent to a torsional couple) are to be applied to the end sections $z = 0, l$ only.

To complete the solution, one has to show that the equation of heat conduction, Equation (5.60), is satisfied. This will be left as an exercise.

- *Problems*

1. Give a proof of the tensor property of the stress components; i.e., show that $s_{ij}' = a_{il}a_{jm}s_{lm}$ under a rotation of the coordinate system, where $a_{il} = \cos(x_i', x_l)$ are the directional cosines.

HINT: From $x_i' = a_{ik}x_k$ it follows that

$$n_i = a_{li}n_l' \qquad \text{and} \qquad \mathbf{g}_j = \left(\frac{\partial \mathbf{r}}{\partial x_m'} + \frac{\partial \mathbf{u}}{\partial x_m'}\right)\frac{\partial x_m'}{\partial x_j} = a_{mj}\mathbf{g}_m'.$$

Substitution into Equation (5.16) completes the proof.

2. Show that the equation of heat conduction is satisfied in the example of Section 5.8.

HINT: Since there are no heat sources present, Equation (5.60) reduces to

$$q_{i,i} \equiv \operatorname{div}\mathbf{q} \equiv \frac{1}{r}\frac{\partial}{\partial r}(rq_r) + \frac{1}{r}\frac{\partial q_\theta}{\partial \theta} + \frac{\partial q_z}{\partial z} = 0.$$

The solution satisfies this equation provided the φ_i are functions of r alone, i.e., do not depend on the temperature $T = T_0 + kz$.

3. Determine heat flow and stresses in an isotropic incompressible cylinder stretched according to $w = az$ and subject to a temperature distribution $\Theta = kz$.

HINT: Due to the incompressibility of the material, the radius r of the cylinder will change to $r + U(r)$. Determine $U(r)$ and obtain u and v. Proceed as in Section 5.8.

---

† Deformed and undeformed radial and circumferential direction are identical here. This is not so for the axial direction where generating lines are deformed into helices.

4. Determine the stresses in an isotropic *compressible* rod of arbitrary cross section stretched to $w = az$ and subjected to a temperature distribution $\Theta = kz$.

HINT: All fibres parallel to the axial direction experience the same unit elongation $\varepsilon_z = a$. Equation (5.9) then gives $2e_{zz} = 2a + a^2$. Comparison with $2e_{zz}$ from Equation (5.7) gives $\partial u / \partial z = \partial v / \partial z = 0$ and, hence, $e_{xz} = e_{yz} = 0$. Cross sections will, therefore, remain plane.

Now, let $u = cx$, $v = cy$, whence $2e_{xx} = 2e_{yy} = 2c + c^2$ and $e_{xy} = 0$. Use Equation (5.32) to find the corresponding stresses:

$$s_{xz} = s_{yz} = s_{xy} = 0 \quad \text{and} \quad s_{xx} = s_{yy} = \frac{\partial W}{\partial I_1} + e_{xx}\frac{\partial W}{\partial I_2} + e_{xx}^2\frac{\partial W}{\partial I_3} = \text{const.}$$

Since the lateral surface of the rod is to be free of applied stress, the constant must vanish. This determines c. The only nonvanishing stress component is s_{zz}.

5. Use the results of the preceding problem to determine the heat flow in the rod.

HINT: Since $\partial \theta / \partial x = \partial \theta / \partial y = 0$, Equation (5.38) gives

$$q_x = q_y = 0, \qquad q_z = k(\varphi_0 + \varphi_1 e_{zz} + \varphi_2 e_{zz}^2).$$

CHAPTER 6

Wave Propagation

Iғ some quantity such as stress, velocity, or temperature gradient experiences a discontinuity (jump) across a surface A, and if the surface moves through the body, we speak of a *wave*, and call A the *wave front*. In particular, depending on the shape of the surface, we may have plane waves, cylindrical waves, spherical waves, etc.

The *speed of propagation* V in the direction of the surface normal **n** is the rate at which the surface A traverses the material. The *strength* of the discontinuity may be characterized by the *amplitude vector* **a**. If **a** is parallel to the surface normal, we have a *longitudinal wave*, if it is normal to **n**, a *transverse wave*. The wave is called *polarized* if the amplitude vector is always parallel to a fixed direction.

The word wave is also used with somewhat different meanings. For instance, one speaks of a *harmonic wave* if a *sinusoidal disturbance* traverses a body. Such waves will be discussed in Section 6.2.

To simplify matters,† we shall restrict ourselves in the following to *one-dimensional plane waves*, i.e., waves propagating in a fixed direction x with displacement, stress, and temperature functions of x and t only. In addition, we shall assume that displacement and displacement gradient connected with the wave are sufficiently small so that it is unnecessary to distinguish between its values at the position of a particle before or after deformation.

Even under these restrictive assumptions, the existence of plane waves in a medium is by no means assured. For instance, if an isotropic body has been prestressed in a nonuniform manner, a disturbance will, in general, not propagate as a *plane* wave.

---

† More general results may be found in reference [24], Section 180 ff. and reference [21], Section 71 ff.

6.1. Jump Conditions

Let the position of the plane wave front A at time t be given by

$$x = \xi(t). \tag{6.1}$$

Then $\dot{\xi} = V$ is the speed of propagation of the wave. Now, consider some function $F(x, t)$. The total rate of change of F as observed from the moving wave front is

$$\frac{dF}{dt} = \frac{\partial F}{\partial t} + V \frac{\partial F}{\partial x}. \tag{6.2}$$

Suppose, now, that F experiences a discontinuity

$$F^+ - F^- = [F] \tag{6.3}$$

at the wave front. Here, F^+ is the value of F immediately ahead of the surface A, and F^- is the value immediately behind A. Then, upon writing Equation (6.2) twice, first for F^+ and then for F^-, and subtracting, one gets

$$\frac{d}{dt}[F] = \left[\frac{\partial F}{\partial t}\right] + V \left[\frac{\partial F}{\partial x}\right]. \tag{6.4}$$

In particular, if F is continuous with discontinuous first derivatives, there follows

$$\left[\frac{\partial F}{\partial t}\right] = -V \left[\frac{\partial F}{\partial x}\right]. \tag{6.5}$$

Replacing F in Equation (6.4) by $\partial F/\partial t$ and $\partial F/\partial x$, respectively, one finds

$$\frac{d}{dt}\left[\frac{\partial F}{\partial t}\right] = \left[\frac{\partial^2 F}{\partial t^2}\right] + V \left[\frac{\partial^2 F}{\partial t \partial x}\right],$$

$$\frac{d}{dt}\left[\frac{\partial F}{\partial x}\right] = \left[\frac{\partial^2 F}{\partial x \partial t}\right] + V \left[\frac{\partial^2 F}{\partial x^2}\right].$$

Now, if F and its first derivatives are continuous with discontinuous second derivatives, then

$$\left[\frac{\partial^2 F}{\partial t^2}\right] = V^2 \left[\frac{\partial^2 F}{\partial x^2}\right] = -V \left[\frac{\partial^2 F}{\partial x \partial t}\right]. \tag{6.6}$$

Jump relations expressed in Equations (6.4) through (6.6) are *kinematical* conditions of compatibility. We apply them to the displacement vector

$$\mathbf{u} = \sum_{m=x,y,z} u_m(x, t)\mathbf{e}_m, \tag{6.7}$$

where $\mathbf{e}_m$ are three orthogonal unit vectors. A wave front across which $\mathbf{u}$ is continuous, but its first derivatives suffer a jump, is called a *singular surface of order* 1. From Equation (6.5), we have on such a surface†

$$[\dot{u}_m] = -V a_m, \qquad a_m = [u_{m,x}] = [\varepsilon_{mx}] \qquad (m = x, y, z), \qquad (6.8)$$

where a_m is a component of the amplitude vector and ε_{mx}, from Equation (2.10a), represents the linearized strain. If $[\dot{u}_x] = 0$, but at least one of the two transverse velocity components $\dot{u}_y$ and $\dot{u}_z$ is discontinuous, the wave front is known as *slip surface*. On the other hand, if $\dot{u}_y$ and $\dot{u}_z$ are continuous, but the normal velocity $\dot{u}_x$ suffers a discontinuity, the surface A is called a *shock surface*.

A *singular surface of order* 2 is defined as a surface across which **u** and its first derivatives are continuous, but its second derivatives are discontinuous. In this case, Equation (6.6) gives for the displacement component u_m

$$[\ddot{u}_m] = V^2 a_m, \qquad [\dot{u}_{m,x}] = [\dot{\varepsilon}_{mx}] = -V a_m, \left.\right\}$$
$$a_m = [u_{m,xx}] = [\varepsilon_{mx,x}]. \qquad\qquad\qquad (6.9)$$

Since the acceleration $\ddot{u}_m$ is now discontinuous, the wave is called an *acceleration wave* or, frequently, a *sound wave*.

We turn now to the *dynamic* jump conditions. Let the stress associated with the small disturbance produced by the wave be denoted by $\sigma_{ij}(x, t)$. If, at time t, we consider the plane surfaces of unit area fixed in space at $x_1 = \xi(t) - \lambda$ and $x_2 = \xi(t) + \lambda$, adjacent to the singular plane A, the law of linear momentum gives for the volume enclosed between x_2 and x_1

$$\lim_{\lambda \to 0} \left\{ \frac{d}{dt} \int_{x_1}^{\xi(t)} \rho \dot{u}_m \, dx + \frac{d}{dt} \int_{\xi(t)}^{x_2} \rho \dot{u}_m \, dx \right\} = [\sigma_{xm}].$$

Performing the differentiation and letting $\lambda \to 0$, we obtain, with $\dot{\xi} = V$ and ρ continuous for small deformations

$$\lim_{\lambda \to 0} \left\{ (V \rho \dot{u}_m)_1 - (V \rho \dot{u}_m)_2 \right\} = -V \rho [\dot{u}_m].$$

Thus,

$$[\sigma_{xm}] = -V \rho [\dot{u}_m]. \qquad (6.10)$$

Combining Equations (6.8) and (6.10), we have

$$[\sigma_{xm}] = \rho V^2 [u_{m,x}], \qquad (6.11)$$

valid for shock waves in any material, independent of the constitutive equation. The latter, if substituted into Equation (6.11), yields the speed of propagation V. We note that, with the stress-strain law depending on the direction of the amplitude vector and on temperature, V will, in general, not be a constant. It will be constant only in the case of polarized waves propagating through a uniform temperature field.

---

† We use the notation introduced in the footnote on p. 71 for the derivatives of a vector.

The equation of motion, Equation (5.14), simplifies here to

$$\sigma_{xm,x} + \rho F_m = \rho \ddot{u}_m.$$

From this, we obtain at once, utilizing Equation (6.9),

$$[\sigma_{xm,x}] = \rho[\ddot{u}_m] = \rho V^2[\varepsilon_{xm,x}]. \tag{6.12}$$

This relation between stress-gradient and strain-gradient is, in general, different from the relation between stress and strain. Therefore, the velocity V for the propagation of an acceleration wave will be different from that of a shock wave with the same direction of amplitude.

In passing, we note that, since the strain is continuous across an acceleration wave, it follows that the stress is also continuous.

The last jump condition to be derived refers to the law of conservation of energy, Equation (5.20). Considering, as above, the volume between two fixed plane surfaces of unit area at $x_1 = \xi(t) - \lambda$ and $x_2 = \xi(t) + \lambda$, and introducing Equation (5.24) into Equation (5.20), we may write

$$\lim_{\lambda \to 0} \left\{ \frac{d}{dt} \int_{x_1}^{\xi(t)} \left(\frac{k}{\rho} + \Phi + TS - \sum_{i=x,y,z} F_i \dot{u}_i \right) \rho \, dV \right.$$

$$\left. + \frac{d}{dt} \int_{\xi(t)}^{x_2} \left(\frac{k}{\rho} + \Phi + TS - \sum_{i=x,y,z} F_i \dot{u}_i \right) \rho \, dV \right\} = \sum_i [\sigma_{xi} \dot{u}_i] - [q_x], \tag{6.13}$$

where

$$k = \frac{1}{2} \sum_{m=x,y,z} \rho \dot{u}_m^2$$

represents the kinetic energy per unit volume. Proceeding as before, we find

$$V \left\{ [k] + \rho[\Phi] + \rho[TS] - \rho \sum_i F_i[\dot{u}_i] \right\} = [q_x] - \sum_i [\sigma_{xi} \dot{u}_i]. \tag{6.14}$$

In a shock wave, T and S may be discontinuous. In an acceleration wave, we require, by definition, that both T and S be continuous, while their first derivatives may exhibit jumps. If, however,

$$[\dot{T}] = 0, \qquad [T_{,x}] = 0,$$

the acceleration wave is called *homothermal*. When, instead,

$$[\dot{S}] = 0, \qquad [S_{,x}] = 0,$$

the wave is called *homentropic*.†

---

† See reference [21], p. 383.

6.2. Example: Plane Waves in an Initially Stressed Medium

We suppose, now, that the initially isotropic body is stretched to uniform finite extensions and is then held in equilibrium by suitable surface tractions. The temperature throughout the body is constant and equal to T_0. It follows that the stresses and the entropy are constant and the heat flux is zero. We denote the coordinates of a particle *after* this initial finite deformation by x, y, z so that

$$x = \lambda x_0, \qquad y = \mu y_0, \qquad z = \mu z_0, \tag{6.15}$$

where x_0, y_0, z_0 are the coordinates of the particle in the unstrained state.

We now superpose a small disturbance in the form of a plane wave propagating in the direction of x.† The coordinates of the particle change, then, to

$$x_1 = x + \hat{\varepsilon} u(x), \qquad y_1 = y + \hat{\varepsilon} v(x), \qquad z_1 = z + \hat{\varepsilon} w(x). \tag{6.16}$$

The parameter $\hat{\varepsilon}$ is supposed to be small. Connected with this deformation will be the temperature

$$T_1 = T_0 + \hat{\varepsilon}\Theta(x). \tag{6.17}$$

We compute all quantities in powers of $\hat{\varepsilon}$ and neglect terms of order higher than the first.

The displacements from the initial unstrained state are

$$u_1 = x_1 - x_0 = (\lambda - 1)x_0 + \hat{\varepsilon} u, \qquad u_2 = y_1 - y_0 = (\mu - 1)y_0 + \hat{\varepsilon} v,$$

$$u_3 = z_1 - z_0 = (\mu - 1)z_0 + \hat{\varepsilon} w.$$

This gives the deformation gradients

$$\left.\begin{aligned}
\frac{\partial u_1}{\partial x_0} &= \lambda - 1 + \hat{\varepsilon}\lambda\frac{\partial u}{\partial x}, & \frac{\partial u_1}{\partial y_0} &= \frac{\partial u_1}{\partial z_0} = 0, \\[2mm]
\frac{\partial u_2}{\partial x_0} &= \hat{\varepsilon}\lambda\frac{\partial v}{\partial x}, & \frac{\partial u_2}{\partial y_0} &= \mu - 1, & \frac{\partial u_2}{\partial z_0} &= 0, \\[2mm]
\frac{\partial u_3}{\partial x_0} &= \hat{\varepsilon}\lambda\frac{\partial w}{\partial x}, & \frac{\partial u_3}{\partial y_0} &= 0, & \frac{\partial u_3}{\partial z_0} &= \mu - 1.
\end{aligned}\right\} \tag{6.18}$$

Substitution of Equations (6.18) into Equations (5.7) yields the strain

---

† For the more general case of a plane wave travelling in an arbitrary direction see reference [25]. Plane waves of finite amplitude are treated in reference [26].

components

$$e_{11} = \frac{\lambda^2 - 1}{2} + \hat{\varepsilon}\lambda^2 \frac{\partial u}{\partial x}, \qquad e_{12} = \hat{\varepsilon}\frac{\lambda\mu}{2}\frac{\partial v}{\partial x}, \qquad e_{13} = \hat{\varepsilon}\frac{\lambda\mu}{2}\frac{\partial w}{\partial x},$$
$$e_{22} = \frac{\mu^2 - 1}{2}, \qquad\qquad e_{23} = 0, \qquad\qquad e_{33} = \frac{\mu^2 - 1}{2}. \tag{6.19}$$

The strain invariants are obtained from Equations (5.31a) as

$$I_1 = \frac{1}{2}(\lambda^2 + 2\mu^2 - 3) + \hat{\varepsilon}\lambda^2 \frac{\partial u}{\partial x},$$
$$I_2 = \frac{(\lambda^2 - 1)^2}{8} + \frac{(\mu^2 - 1)^2}{4} + \hat{\varepsilon}\frac{\lambda^2(\lambda^2 - 1)}{2}\frac{\partial u}{\partial x}, \tag{6.20}$$
$$I_3 = \frac{(\lambda^2 - 1)^3}{24} + \frac{(\mu^2 - 1)^3}{12} + \hat{\varepsilon}\frac{\lambda^2(\lambda^2 - 1)^2}{4}\frac{\partial u}{\partial x}.$$

The stress consists of two parts: constant stresses s^0_{ij} connected with the uniform finite extensions of Equations (6.15) with

$$s^0_{11} = s_1, \qquad s^0_{22} = s^0_{33} = s_2, \qquad s^0_{12} = s^0_{23} = s^0_{31} = 0, \tag{6.21}$$

and stresses $\hat{\varepsilon}s_{ij}(x)$ connected with the disturbance. The constitutive equation (5.32) relates the total stress $s^0_{ij} + \hat{\varepsilon}s_{ij}(x)$ to the total strain e_{ij}. If the right-hand side of Equation (5.32) is expanded in a Taylor series in powers of $\hat{\varepsilon}$, we obtain

$$s^0_{ij} + \hat{\varepsilon}s_{ij} = \Phi_1\delta_{ij} + \Phi_2 e_{ij} + \Phi_3 e_{ik}e_{jk}, \tag{6.22}$$

where

$$\Phi_i = A_i + \hat{\varepsilon}\left(B_i \frac{\partial u}{\partial x} + C_i\Theta\right) + \cdots, \tag{6.23}$$

$$A_i = \frac{\partial W}{\partial I_i}, \qquad B_i = \lambda^2\left(\frac{\partial^2 W}{\partial I_1 \partial I_i} + \frac{\lambda^2 - 1}{2}\frac{\partial^2 W}{\partial I_2 \partial I_i} + \frac{(\lambda^2 - 1)^2}{4}\frac{\partial^2 W}{\partial I_3 \partial I_i}\right),$$
$$C_i = \frac{\partial^2 W}{\partial T \partial I_i}. \tag{6.24}$$

The coefficients A_i, B_i, C_i are to be evaluated at $\hat{\varepsilon} = 0$ and are, therefore, constants. Comparing coefficients of $\hat{\varepsilon}$ on both sides of the constitutive equation (6.22) and utilizing Equations (6.19), we find the following stresses in the wave

$$
\left.\begin{aligned}
s_{xx} &= \left[B_1 + A_2\lambda^2 + B_2\frac{\lambda^2 - 1}{2} + A_3\lambda^2(\lambda^2 - 1) + B_3\left(\frac{\lambda^2 - 1}{2}\right)^2\right]\frac{\partial u}{\partial x} \\
&\quad + \left[C_1 + C_2\frac{\lambda^2 - 1}{2} + C_3\left(\frac{\lambda^2 - 1}{2}\right)^2\right]\Theta, \\
s_{xy} &= \left[A_2\frac{\lambda\mu}{2} + A_3\frac{\lambda^2 + \mu^2 - 2}{4}\lambda\mu\right]\frac{\partial v}{\partial x}, \\
s_{xz} &= \left[A_2\frac{\lambda\mu}{2} + A_3\frac{\lambda^2 + \mu^2 - 2}{4}\lambda\mu\right]\frac{\partial w}{\partial x},
\end{aligned}\right\} \quad (6.25)
$$

$$
\left.\begin{aligned}
s_{yy} = s_{zz} &= \left[B_1 + B_2\frac{\mu^2 - 1}{2} + B_3\left(\frac{\mu^2 - 1}{2}\right)^2\right]\frac{\partial u}{\partial x} \\
&\quad + \left[C_1 + C_2\frac{\mu^2 - 1}{2} + C_3\left(\frac{\mu^2 - 1}{2}\right)^2\right]\Theta,
\end{aligned}\right\} \quad (6.26)
$$

$$
s_{yz} = 0.
$$

As the next step in the derivation of the basic relations of the problem, the three equations of motion will be established. Replacing x_1, x_2, x_3 in Equations (5.14a) by x_0, y_0, z_0, respectively, writing $s_{ij}^0 + \hat{\varepsilon}s_{ij}$ instead of s_{ij}, substituting Equations (6.18) and (6.21), and retaining terms up to order 1 in $\hat{\varepsilon}$, one finds that Equations (5.14a) become

$$
\left.\begin{aligned}
\lambda\frac{\partial}{\partial x}\left(\lambda s_1\frac{\partial u}{\partial x} + \lambda s_{xx}\right) &= \rho_0\frac{\partial^2 u}{\partial t^2}, \\
\lambda\frac{\partial}{\partial x}\left(\lambda s_1\frac{\partial v}{\partial x} + \mu s_{xy}\right) &= \rho_0\frac{\partial^2 v}{\partial t^2}, \\
\lambda\frac{\partial}{\partial x}\left(\lambda s_1\frac{\partial w}{\partial x} + \mu s_{xz}\right) &= \rho_0\frac{\partial^2 w}{\partial t^2},
\end{aligned}\right\} \quad (6.27)
$$

where ρ_0 is the mass density in the unstressed state. After substitution of Equations (6.25), the equations become

$$
a\frac{\partial^2 u}{\partial x^2} + b\frac{\partial\Theta}{\partial x} = \rho_0\frac{\partial^2 u}{\partial t^2}, \quad (6.28)
$$

$$
c\frac{\partial^2 v}{\partial x^2} = \rho_0\frac{\partial^2 v}{\partial t^2}, \qquad c\frac{\partial^2 w}{\partial x^2} = \rho_0\frac{\partial^2 w}{\partial t^2}, \quad (6.29)
$$

where

$$a = \lambda^2 \left[s_1 + B_1 + A_2\lambda^2 + B_2 \frac{\lambda^2 - 1}{2} + A_3\lambda^2(\lambda^2 - 1) + B_3\left(\frac{\lambda^2 - 1}{2}\right)^2 \right],$$

$$b = \lambda^2 \left[C_1 + C_2 \frac{\lambda^2 - 1}{2} + C_3\left(\frac{\lambda^2 - 1}{2}\right)^2 \right], \tag{6.30}$$

$$c = \lambda^2 s_1 + \frac{\lambda^2\mu^2}{4} [2A_2 + A_3(\lambda^2 + \mu^2 - 2)].$$

Since v and w are displacements perpendicular to the direction x of the wave propagation, Equations (6.29) represent *transverse* (or *shearing*) *waves*. We note that these waves are not influenced by the temperature variation $\Theta(x, t)$, in contradistinction to the *longitudinal wave* $u(x, t)$ determined by Equation (6.28).

Applying Equations (6.9) to Equations (6.29), we obtain for the speed of propagation V_T of transverse sound waves in the prestressed medium

$$V_T = \sqrt{\frac{c}{\rho_0}}. \tag{6.31}$$

Equation (6.28) contains two unknown functions: displacement $u(x, t)$ and temperature $\Theta(x, t)$. The missing second equation is, of course, the equation of heat flow, Equation (5.37). Expanding the right-hand side of Equation (5.38) in powers of $\hat{\varepsilon}$, we get

$$q_i = \hat{\varepsilon} \sum_j D_{ij}\Theta_{,j} = \hat{\varepsilon}D_{i1} \frac{\partial\Theta}{\partial x}, \tag{6.32}$$

where the constants

$$D_{i1} = \varphi_0\delta_{i1} + \varphi_1 e_{i1} + \varphi_2 \sum_k e_{ik}e_{k1} \tag{6.33}$$

are to be evaluated at $\hat{\varepsilon} = 0$. Substituting Equation (6.32) into Equation (5.37) and noting that

$$\frac{\partial}{\partial T}(s_{ij}^0 + \hat{\varepsilon}s_{ij}) = \hat{\varepsilon} \frac{\partial s_{ij}}{\partial T} = \frac{\partial s_{ij}}{\partial\Theta},$$

we find

$$\hat{\varepsilon}D_{11} \frac{\partial^2\Theta}{\partial x^2} = (T_0 + \hat{\varepsilon}\Theta)\left(\frac{\partial s_{ij}}{\partial\Theta} \dot{e}_{ij} + \frac{\partial^2 W}{\partial T^2} \hat{\varepsilon}\dot{\Theta}\right),$$

or, utilizing Equations (6.19) and (6.25),

$$k_1 \frac{\partial^2\Theta}{\partial x^2} = k_2 \frac{\partial\Theta}{\partial t} - T_0 b \frac{\partial^2 u}{\partial t\partial x}, \tag{6.34}$$

with

$$k_1 = -D_{11}, \qquad k_2 = -T_0\left(\frac{\partial^2 W}{\partial T^2}\right)_{\hat{\varepsilon}=0}. \tag{6.35}$$

Equations (6.28) and (6.34) are the basic equations of the longitudinal wave. Comparing Equations (6.9) and (6.28), we note immediately that the speed of a homothermal longitudinal acceleration wave is

$$V_L = \sqrt{\frac{a}{\rho_0}}. \tag{6.36}$$

In order to study Equations (6.28) and (6.34) in more detail, we now introduce a particular solution representing *harmonic waves*,

$$u(x, t) = u_0 \exp [i(\eta x - \omega t)], \qquad \Theta(x, t) = \Theta_0 \exp [i(\eta x - \omega t)], \quad (6.37a)$$

where η and ω are unknown, in general complex, constants, and $i = \sqrt{-1}$.

The importance of this solution is, to some measure, due to the fact that, by Fourier series theory, any propagating disturbance may be resolved into components of the form of Equation (6.37a). Putting $\eta = p + iq$, $\omega = r - is$, we write

$$u(x, t) = u_0 \exp \{-(qx + st)\} \begin{array}{l} \cos p(x - Vt), \\ \sin p(x - Vt), \end{array} \tag{6.37b}$$

and a corresponding expression for the temperature Θ. Thus, $V = r/p$ represents the speed of propagation and $l = 2\pi/p$ is the wave length, i.e., twice the distance between two adjacent zeros of u. The wave is, in general, attenuated: its amplitude $u_0 \exp \{-(qx + st)\}$ decreases exponentially with time t at a fixed point x, or with distance x at a fixed time t.

Since the speed of propagation V will, in general, depend on the frequency r, different components of a wave will travel at different speeds leading to *dispersion* of the wave, distorting its shape. However, even though the shape of the wave is not preserved as it moves through the body, discontinuities may travel at distinct velocities.

Substituting Equations (6.37a) into Equations (6.28) and (6.34), we obtain

$$(\rho_0\omega^2 - a\eta^2)u_0 + ib\eta\Theta_0 = 0,$$

$$T_0b\omega\eta u_0 + (ik_2\omega - k_1\eta^2)\Theta_0 = 0.$$

For a nontrivial solution, the determinant of these two equations must vanish:

$$i\rho_0k_2\omega^3 - \rho_0k_1\omega^2\eta^2 - ik_2a\omega\eta^2 + ak_1\eta^4 - iT_0b^2\omega\eta^2 = 0. \tag{6.38}$$

For convenience, we introduce dimensionless quantities†

$$\nu = \frac{\omega}{\omega^*}, \qquad \beta = \frac{\eta V_L}{\omega^*}, \tag{6.39}$$

where V_L is given by Equation (6.36), and

$$\omega^* = \frac{k_2}{k_1} V_L^2 \tag{6.40}$$

is known as *characteristic frequency* of the medium. Equation (6.38) then goes over into

$$(\beta^2 - \nu^2)(\nu + i\beta^2) + \varepsilon\beta^2\nu = 0. \tag{6.41}$$

The parameter

$$\varepsilon = \frac{T_0 b^2}{\rho_0 k_2 V_L^2} \tag{6.42}$$

represents the coupling between temperature and displacement. In general, ε is very small.‡

If we regard ν in Equation (6.41) as a fixed real constant, i.e., if we consider *waves of an assigned frequency*, we have a quadratic equation for β^2 with roots $\pm\beta_1$, $\pm\beta_2$, where

$$\beta_{1,2} = \frac{\sqrt{\nu}}{2}\left[\sqrt{\nu + i(1 + \varepsilon) + (1 + i)\sqrt{2\nu}} \pm \sqrt{\nu + i(1 + \varepsilon) - (1 + i)\sqrt{2\nu}}\right]. \tag{6.43}$$

Separating β and, hence, η into its real and imaginary parts, $\eta = p + iq$, we may rewrite the exponent in Equation (6.37a) in the form Equation (6.37b),

$$i(\eta x - \omega t) = -qx + ip(x - Vt) \qquad (x \geqslant 0), \tag{6.44}$$

where q is the *attenuation coefficient* and $V = \omega/p$ represents the *phase velocity*. Convenient expressions for $q_{1,2}$ and $V_{1,2}$ may be obtained from Equation (6.43) by using series expansions§ in powers of ε or, preferably, of ν, since the latter is much smaller than ε. We restate, here, the expansions

---

† See reference [27] where, however, only the unstressed Hookean solid is treated.
‡ Some values for unstressed metals are given in reference [27].
§ See reference [27].

in powers of ν:

$$
\left.
\begin{aligned}
V_1 &= V_L\sqrt{1+\varepsilon}\left[1 - \frac{\varepsilon(4-3\varepsilon)}{8(1+\varepsilon)^4}\nu^2 + \cdots\right], \\[2mm]
q_1 &= \frac{\varepsilon\omega^*\nu^2}{2V_L(1+\varepsilon)^{5/2}}\left[1 - \frac{8-20\varepsilon+5\varepsilon^2}{8(1+\varepsilon)^4}\nu^2 + \cdots\right], \\[2mm]
V_2 &= V_L\sqrt{\frac{2\nu}{1+\varepsilon}}\left[1 - \frac{\varepsilon}{2(1+\varepsilon)^2}\nu + \frac{\varepsilon(4+\varepsilon)}{8(1+\varepsilon)^4}\nu^2 + \cdots\right], \\[2mm]
q_2 &= \frac{\omega^*}{V_L}\sqrt{\frac{\nu}{2}(1+\varepsilon)}\left[1 - \frac{\varepsilon}{2(1+\varepsilon)^2}\nu - \frac{\varepsilon(4-\varepsilon)}{8(1+\varepsilon)^4}\nu^2 + \cdots\right].
\end{aligned}
\right\}
\tag{6.45}
$$

Waves with frequencies close to ω^* and above are severely attenuated and, hence, cannot be observed in experiments.

If coupling between displacement and temperature is neglected, $\varepsilon = 0$, Equations (6.45) reduce to

$$
V_1 = V_L, \qquad q_1 = 0, \qquad V_2 = V_L\sqrt{2\nu}, \qquad q_2 = \sqrt{\frac{\omega}{2}\frac{k_2}{k_1}}.
\tag{6.46}
$$

The two Equations (6.28) and (6.34) separate in this case, giving $\beta_1 = \nu$, $\beta_2 = \sqrt{i\nu}$. Thus, V_1 and q_1 belong to the displacement wave, while V_2 and q_2 refer to the temperature wave. We note that, in the uncoupled case, the displacement wave is not damped and travels with frequency-independent speed. The thermal wave is attenuated and, since its phase velocity depends on the frequency, it is subject to dispersion.

Finally, we consider *waves of assigned length* by regarding η as a real given quantity. Equation (6.41) is then a cubic in ν. Its three roots may be written in the form

$$
\nu_1 = f - ig, \qquad \nu_2 = -f - ig, \qquad \nu_3 = -ih,
\tag{6.47}
$$

where f, g, h are real. Using series expansions in powers of ε, one finds,[†]

$$
\left.
\begin{aligned}
f &= \beta\left[1 + \frac{1}{2(1+\beta^2)}\varepsilon - \frac{1-6\beta^2+\beta^4}{8(1+\beta^2)^3}\varepsilon^2 + \cdots\right], \\[2mm]
g &= \frac{\beta^2\varepsilon}{2(1+\beta^2)}\left[1 - \frac{1-\beta^2}{(1+\beta^2)^2}\varepsilon + \cdots\right], \\[2mm]
h &= \beta^2\left[1 - \frac{1}{1+\beta^2}\varepsilon + \frac{1-\beta^2}{(1+\beta^2)^3}\varepsilon^2 + \cdots\right].
\end{aligned}
\right\}
\tag{6.48}
$$

† See reference [27].

The series converge uniformly for all $\beta \geqslant 0$. Upon putting $\varepsilon = 0$, one obtains Equations (6.46).

6.3. Example: Pressure Shock on the Surface of a Semi-Infinite Body

The semi-infinite body $x \geqslant 0$ is initially free of stress and at uniform temperature T_0. At time $t = 0$, a uniform pressure p is suddenly applied at the surface $x = 0$ and kept constant thereafter.

The pressure jump will create a shock wave and, due to dissipation of heat, the corresponding stress discontinuity $[\sigma_{xx}]$ will be attenuated as it travels from the surface into the body. Displacement and temperature are again governed by Equations (6.28) and (6.34), together with appropriate initial and boundary conditions.† If we assume the surface perfectly insulated against loss of heat, these conditions are,

$$\left.\begin{array}{llllll} \text{for} & t = 0: & u = 0, & \Theta = 0 & \text{in} & x > 0, \\ \text{for} & t > 0: & \sigma_{xx} = -p, & \dfrac{\partial \Theta}{\partial x} = 0 & \text{in} & x = 0. \end{array}\right\} \quad (6.49)$$

The stress-strain law follows from Equations (6.25) and (6.30),

$$\sigma_{xx} = a\frac{\partial u}{\partial x} + b\Theta, \qquad \sigma_{xy} = c\frac{\partial v}{\partial x}, \qquad \sigma_{xz} = c\frac{\partial w}{\partial x}. \qquad (6.50)$$

Therefore, the elastic potential W reads,

$$W = 2cI_2 + \frac{a - 2c}{2}I_1^2 + bI_1\Theta - \frac{k_2}{T_0}\Theta^2, \qquad (6.51)$$

with

$$I_1 = \frac{\partial u}{\partial x}, \qquad I_2 = \frac{1}{2}\left(\frac{\partial u}{\partial x}\right)^2 + \frac{1}{4}\left(\frac{\partial v}{\partial x}\right)^2 + \frac{1}{4}\left(\frac{\partial w}{\partial x}\right)^2. \qquad (6.52)$$

The complete solution of wave-propagation problems of the type stated above offers substantial difficulties. Usually, integral transform techniques are applied.‡ However, it invariably turns out that the inverse transform cannot be performed in an exact manner. It is then necessary to resort to approximate methods or to numerical procedures.

The problem becomes much simpler if attention is focussed on the behavior of the discontinuities at the wavefront only.§ This will be done in the

---

† Since the body is now free of stress in its initial state, we have $\lambda = \mu = 1$, $s_1 = s_2 = 0$.
‡ A critical survey of the existing literature is given in reference [28].
§ See references [29] and [30]. A detailed account is given in reference [31].

following pages. Since shearing waves are independent of longitudinal waves, they will be disregarded, $v = w = 0$.

First, we note, by comparing Equations (6.50) and (6.11) with $m = x$, that the temperature Θ will be continuous at the front of the shock wave, and that

$$[\sigma_{xx}] = \rho V^2 \left[\frac{\partial u}{\partial x}\right], \qquad V = \sqrt{\frac{a}{\rho}}. \tag{6.53}$$

Furthermore, since u will be continuous across the wavefront, Equation (6.5) with $F = u$ holds:

$$\left[\frac{\partial u}{\partial t}\right] = -V\left[\frac{\partial u}{\partial x}\right] \quad \text{and, hence,} \quad \frac{d}{dt}\left[\frac{\partial u}{\partial t}\right] = -V\frac{d}{dt}\left[\frac{\partial u}{\partial x}\right]. \tag{6.54}$$

In addition, we have from Equation (6.4) with $F = \partial u/\partial x$ and $F = \partial u/\partial t$, respectively,

$$\frac{d}{dt}\left[\frac{\partial u}{\partial x}\right] = \left[\frac{\partial^2 u}{\partial x \partial t}\right] + V\left[\frac{\partial^2 u}{\partial x^2}\right],$$

$$\frac{d}{dt}\left[\frac{\partial u}{\partial t}\right] = \left[\frac{\partial^2 u}{\partial t^2}\right] + V\left[\frac{\partial^2 u}{\partial x \partial t}\right].$$

Combining the three equations leads to the kinematic relation

$$-2V\frac{d}{dt}\left[\frac{\partial u}{\partial x}\right] = \left[\frac{\partial^2 u}{\partial t^2}\right] - V^2\left[\frac{\partial^2 u}{\partial x^2}\right]. \tag{6.55}$$

Equation (6.28) gives the dynamic condition

$$\left[\frac{\partial^2 u}{\partial t^2}\right] = V^2\left[\frac{\partial^2 u}{\partial x^2}\right] + \frac{b}{\rho}\left[\frac{\partial \Theta}{\partial x}\right].$$

Hence,

$$\frac{d}{dt}\left[\frac{\partial u}{\partial x}\right] = -\frac{b}{2\rho V}\left[\frac{\partial \Theta}{\partial x}\right]. \tag{6.56}$$

A second relation between the two discontinuities $[\partial u/\partial x]$ and $[\partial \Theta/\partial x]$ may be obtained from Equation (6.14) which reads, here,

$$[q_x] = \left[\sigma_{xx}\frac{\partial u}{\partial t}\right] + V\left\{\frac{\rho}{2}\left[\frac{\partial u}{\partial t}\right]^2 + [W] + \rho T[S]\right\}.$$

Substituting from Equations (6.50), (6.51), (6.52), using $T = T_0 + \Theta$ and

$$S = \frac{-1}{\rho}\frac{\partial W}{\partial \Theta} = -\frac{b}{\rho}\frac{\partial u}{\partial x} + \frac{2k_2}{\rho T_0}\Theta,$$

we get

$$[q_x] = a\left[\frac{\partial u}{\partial x}\frac{\partial u}{\partial t}\right] + b\Theta\left[\frac{\partial u}{\partial t}\right] + V\left\{\frac{\rho}{2}\left[\frac{\partial u}{\partial t}\right]^2 + c\left[\frac{\partial u}{\partial x}\right]^2 + \frac{a - 2c}{2}\left[\frac{\partial u}{\partial x}\right]^2\right.$$
$$\left. + b\Theta\left[\frac{\partial u}{\partial x}\right] - b(T_0 + \Theta)\left[\frac{\partial u}{\partial x}\right]\right\}.$$

Eliminating $[\partial u/\partial t]$ by means of the first of Equations (6.54) and using $V^2\rho = a$, there follows

$$[q_x] = -bVT\left[\frac{\partial u}{\partial x}\right],$$

or, if Θ is neglected in comparison with T_0,

$$[q_x] = -bVT_0\left[\frac{\partial u}{\partial x}\right]. \tag{6.57}$$

Equation (6.32) connects the discontinuity $[q_x]$ of the heat flux with the discontinuity of the temperature gradient,

$$[q_x] = -k_1\left[\frac{\partial \Theta}{\partial x}\right].$$

Thus, we have the desired second relation as

$$\left[\frac{\partial \Theta}{\partial x}\right] = \frac{bVT_0}{k_1}\left[\frac{\partial u}{\partial x}\right]. \tag{6.58}$$

Eliminating, now, $[\partial u/\partial x]$ and $[\partial\Theta/\partial x]$ from Equations (6.53), (6.56), and (6.58), the following differential equation for the discontinuity of the normal stress $[\sigma_{xx}]$ propagating with speed V is obtained,

$$\frac{d}{dt}[\sigma_{xx}] + \kappa[\sigma_{xx}] = 0, \qquad \kappa = \frac{b^2 T_0}{2\rho k_1}. \tag{6.59}$$

With initial condition $[\sigma_{xx}] = -p$ at $t = 0$, the solution of this equation is

$$[\sigma_{xx}] = -pe^{-\kappa t}. \tag{6.60}$$

If $\kappa = 0$, no coupling exists and the temperature field is not influenced by the deformation. The stress discontinuity would then always retain its full value p as it travels through the body. In reality, κ is a relatively large number† for most materials and the discontinuity is damped out over a very short distance.

---

† Using Equations (6.40) and (6.42), we may write $\kappa = (\varepsilon/2)\omega^*$.

- *Problems*

1. For the problem of Section 6.2, show that heat flows in the direction of x only.

HINT: Use Equations (6.32) and (6.33) and show that $D_{i1} = 0$ for all $i \neq 1$.

2. Show that Equation (6.43) represents the solution of Equation (6.41).

HINT: Rewrite Equation (6.41) in the form $\beta^4 - [\nu + i(1 + \varepsilon)]\nu\beta^2 + i\nu^3 = 0$, determine β^2 and check with β^2 from Equation (6.43).

3. Determine V_T and V_L from Equations (6.31) and (6.36), respectively, for the unstressed Hookean solid.

HINT: Use Equation (5.51) and substitute into Equations (6.24) and (6.30) to find

$$V_T = \sqrt{\frac{G}{\rho_0}}, \qquad V_L = \sqrt{\frac{2(1 - \nu)G}{\rho_0(1 - 2\nu)}}.$$

4. Equations (6.29) show that shear waves are not influenced by the temperature. Hence, a discontinuity of the shearing stress $[\sigma_{xy}] = \tau$, applied at the surface $x = 0$, would remain undamped as it travels through the body. Use the method of Section 6.3 to prove this, and determine the corresponding discontinuity $[\partial v/\partial t]$.

HINT: Put $u = w = 0$ in Equations (6.50) through (6.52) and use the fact that v is continuous across the wave front. Find $[\dot{v}] = -\tau/V_T\rho_0$.

Bibliography

Bibliography

1. SOKOLNIKOFF, I. S. *Mathematical Theory of Elasticity*, 2nd ed. New York: McGraw-Hill Book Co., 1956.
2. GREEN, A. E., and W. ZERNA. *Theoretical Elasticity*. Oxford: Oxford University Press, 1954.
3. PRAGER, W. *Introduction to the Mechanics of Continua*. Boston: Ginn and Company, 1961.
4. CARSLAW, H. S., and J. C. JAEGER. *Conduction of Heat in Solids*, 2nd ed. Oxford: Clarendon Press, 1959.
5. CHURCHILL, R. V. *Operational Mathematics*, 2nd ed. New York: McGraw-Hill Book Co., 1958.
6. ERDÉLYI *et al*. *Tables of Integral Transforms*, Vol. I. New York: McGraw-Hill Book Co., Inc., 1954.
7. BOLEY, B. A., and J. H. WEINER. *Theory of Thermal Stresses*. New York: John Wiley & Sons, Inc., 1960.
8. EUBANKS, R. A., and E. STERNBERG. "On the Completeness of the Boussinesq-Papkovich Stress Functions," *J. Rational Mech. Anal.*, 5 (1956), 735.
9. MINDLIN, R. D. "Note on the Galerkin and Papkovich Stress Functions," *Bull. Am. Math. Soc.*, 42 (1936), 373.
10. NOWACKI, W. *Thermoelasticity*. Oxford: Pergamon Press, 1962.
11. STERNBERG, E., and E. L. MCDOWELL. "On the Steady-State Thermo-Elastic Problem for the Half-Space," *Qu. Appl. Math.*, 14 (1957), 381.
12. MASSONNET, C. "Two-Dimensional Problems," in W. Flügge (ed.), *Handbook of Engineering Mechanics*. New York: McGraw-Hill Book Co., 1962.
13. PARKUS, H. "Thermal Stresses," in W. Flügge (ed.), *Handbook of Engineering Mechanics*. New York: McGraw-Hill Book Co., 1962.
14. RADOK, J. R. M. "Complex-Variable Approach," in W. Flügge (ed.), *Handbook of Engineering Mechanics*. New York: McGraw-Hill Book Co., 1962.
15. MUSKHELISHVILI, N. I. *Some Basic Problems of the Theory of Elasticity*. Groningen: Noordhoff, 1953.

16. FLORENCE, A. L., and J. N. GOODIER. "Thermal Stress at Spherical Cavities and Circular Holes in Uniform Heat Flow," *J. Appl. Mech.*, *26* (1959), 293.

17. MANSFIELD, E. H. *The Bending and Stretching of Plates.* Oxford: Pergamon Press, 1964.

18. DAS, Y. C., and D. R. NAVARATNA. "Thermal Bending of Rectangular Plate," *J. Aerospace Sci.*, *29* (1962), 1397.

19. VAN DER NEUT, A. "Buckling Caused by Thermal Stresses," in N. J. Hoff (ed.), *Temperature Effects in Aircraft Structures.* Oxford: Pergamon Press, 1958.

20. JOHNS, D. J. *Thermal Stress Analysis.* Oxford: Pergamon Press, 1965.

21. TRUESDELL, C., and W. NOLL. "The Non-Linear Field Theories of Mechanics," *Encyclopedia of Physics.* Vol. III/3. Berlin: Springer-Verlag, 1965.

22. EVANS, R. J., and K. S. PISTER. "Constitutive Equations for a Class of Nonlinear Elastic Solids," *Int. J. Solids Structures*, *2* (1966), 427.

23. GREEN, A. E., and J. E. ADKINS. *Large Elastic Deformations.* Oxford: Clarendon Press, 1960.

24. TRUESDELL, C., and R. TOUPIN. "The Classical Field Theories," *Encyclopedia of Physics*, Vol. III/1. Berlin: Springer-Verlag, 1960.

25. FLAVIN, J. N., and A. E. GREEN. "Plane Thermo-Elastic Waves in an Initially Stressed Medium," *J. Mech. Phys. Solids*, *9* (1961), 179.

26. JOHN, F. "Plane Elastic Waves of Finite Amplitude. Hadamard Materials and Harmonic Materials." *Comm. Pure Appl. Math.*, *19* (1966), 309.

27. CHADWICK, P. "Thermoelasticity. The Dynamical Theory," in I. N. Sneddon and R. Hill (eds.), *Progress in Solid Mechanics*, Vol. I. Amsterdam: North-Holland Publishing Co., 1960.

28. ZIEGLER, F. "Ebene Wellenausbreitung im Halbraum bei Zufallserregung und Kopplung zwischen Spannungs- und Temperaturfeld," *Acta Mechanica*, *2* (1966), 307.

29. BOLEY, B. A. "Discontinuities in Integral-Transform Solutions," *Qu. Appl. Math.*, 19 (1962), 273.

30. ACHENBACH, J. D. "The Propagation of Stress Discontinuities According to the Coupled Equations of Thermoelasticity," *Acta Mechanica*, *3* (1967), 342.

31. CHADWICK, P., and B. POWDRILL. "Singular Surfaces in Linear Thermoelasticity," *Int. J. Engng. Sci.*, *3* (1965), 561.

Index

Index

111

THIS BOOK WAS SET IN
TIMES ROMAN TYPE
BY THE
UNIVERSITIES PRESS.
IT WAS DESIGNED BY THE STAFF OF
BLAISDELL PUBLISHING COMPANY.